McDougal, Littell
Building English Skills

Blue Level

Skills Practice Book

Purple Level
Yellow Level
BLUE LEVEL
Orange Level
Green Level
Red Level
Gold Level
Silver Level
Aqua Level
Brown Level
Plum Level
Pink Level
Cherry Level (K)

McDougal, Littell & Company

Evanston, Illinois
New York   Dallas   Sacramento

Special Features of This Skills Practice Book

- It contains thousands of skill-building exercises in composition, vocabulary, grammar, usage, capitalization, punctuation, spelling, and good manuscript form.

- Each page is a self-contained unit. It contains a brief explanation, followed by an average of twenty reinforcing exercises.

- Each page focuses on one—and only one—topic or skill.

- Key words and phrases are printed in bold face for greater clarity and ease of use.

- A comprehensive review lesson follows each major section of the text.

This Skills Practice Book was conceived and developed by the Staff of McDougal, Littell & Company:

Joy Littell, Editorial Director

Kathleen Laya, Administrative Editor

Geraldine Macsai, Managing Editor

Bonnie Dobkin, Director of Secondary English

Robert D. Shepherd, Associate Editor

Debbie Costello, Assistant Designer

Acknowledgments

The New Yorker Magazine, Inc.: For "Bears" by Adrienne Rich, from *The Diamond Cutters and Other Poems* (Harper & Row). Copyright © 1954, 1982 The New Yorker Magazine, Inc.

Simon & Schuster, Inc.: For the entry *allegiance*, from *Webster's New World Dictionary*, Students Edition: Copyright © 1981 by Simon & Schuster, Inc.

ISBN: 0-86609-310-9

Copyright © 1985, 1981, 1977 by McDougal, Littell & Company
Box 1667, Evanston, Illinois 60204
All rights reserved. Printed in the United States of America

Contents

Composition

Grammar and Usage

Using Context Clues

Often you can find a clue to the meaning of an unfamiliar word by studying the **context** in which the word is used. The following context clues are among the most common: *definition* or *restatement*, *example*, *comparison*, and *contrast*.

Using Context Clues. Tell what type of context clue is given in each of the following sentences. The clue may be a *definition* or *restatement*, an *example*, a *comparison*, or a *contrast*. Then, based on this context clue, write a definition of the italicized word.

1. *Toxicology* is the scientific study of poisons. _____

_____

2. Mr. Boronowski loves to talk, and his friends are similarly *loquacious*.

_____

3. When the new air pollution law was announced, industry officials *lamented*. Environ-

mentalists, on the other hand, rejoiced. _____

_____

4. A love of computer games was the *nexus*, or connection, that held the friends together.

_____

5. Like its cousin, the eagle, the *peregrine* has keen eyesight and a powerful beak.

_____

6. Many United Nations employees are *polyglots*. Ms. Simpson, for example, speaks five

languages fluently. _____

_____

7. Andrew is one of the most *supercilious* people I know. His brother, in contrast, is quite

humble and meek. _____

_____

8. This restaurant serves many *pasta* dishes, including spaghetti, lasagna, and manicotti.

_____

9. *Partridges* are European quaillike game birds. _____

_____

10. *Arachnids*, such as spiders and scorpions, have four pairs of legs. _____

_____

Inferring Word Meanings

To determine the meaning of an unfamiliar word, you will often have to read between the lines. That is, you will have to use inference. **Inference** is the process of analyzing facts in order to draw a conclusion.

To **infer** the meaning of an unfamiliar word, first identify the main idea in the passage you are reading. Then, look for cause and effect relationships and for implied comparisons and contrasts. Finally, choose a meaning for the unfamiliar word that makes sense given the ideas expressed in the rest of the passage.

Inferring the Meanings of Words. Study the ideas expressed in each of the following passages. Then, use inference to determine the meaning of the italicized word in each passage. Circle the closest synonym of the italicized word.

1.   The *prognostications* of our local weather forecaster are nearly always accurate. Therefore, when she predicted rain on Saturday, we canceled our plans to go to the beach. Sure enough, Saturday was one of the rainiest days we've had all summer.

    a. complaints   b. television station   c. plans   d. predictions

2.   An inventor must be *persevering* enough to stick to his or her research despite many false starts and failures. For example, Thomas Edison wasn't able to create a workable light bulb overnight. In fact, this invention took Edison over two years to perfect. Edison's major problem was finding a material for the inside of the bulb. He needed a material that would glow for hours without burning up. After trying hundreds of substances, Edison eventually hit upon using carbonized thread, which is simply sewing thread that has been burned to ash. The carbonized thread worked very well, and the electric light was born.

    a. well-respected   b. persistent   c. happy   d. puzzled

3.   For days the boat drifted on the open sea. On all sides there was nothing but water stretching to the horizon. It was a scene as *desolate* as a desert or lunar landscape, without even an occasional gull to remind the crew of the bustling port they had left behind.

    a. complete   b. frightening   c. deserted   d. beautiful

4.   The *progenitor* of modern methods of criminal investigation was a Frenchman named François-Eugene Vidocq. Vidocq was one of the first detectives to use fingerprints to identify criminals. He was also the first to introduce handwriting analysis as an investigative technique. Under his direction, the French Sûrêté Nationale became a model for other law enforcement agencies, including Scotland Yard and the F.B.I.

    a. creator   b. user   c. investigator   d. ancestor

5.   Hiking in the wilderness has its disadvantages. When Jack gashed his leg on a sharp branch, he had to *swathe* it with strips of cloth torn from his shirt until he got back to the campsite. Only then could he tend to the cut properly.

    a. stitch   b. wrap   c. tighten   d. blend

6.   Clara decided that nothing would *impede* her in her search for a better job. She was determined to overcome the biases against her youth and her lack of experience. Even after numerous rejections, she continued to send out her résumé and to make phone calls to prospective employers.

    a. hinder   b. help   c. contribute   d. formulate

Prefixes and Base Words

A **base word** is a complete word to which another word part may be added. A **prefix** is a word part that is added to the beginning of another word part or complete word. Many words in English are made by combining prefixes and base words.

PREFIX	BASE WORD	NEW WORD
mis- +	interpret	= misinterpret
re- +	locate	= relocate

The following prefixes are useful to know because each has a single meaning:

PREFIXES HAVING A SINGLE MEANING

bene-	= good	**equi-**	= equal	**mal-**	= bad
circum-	= around	**extra-**	= outside	**mis-**	= wrong
com-	= with,	**inter-**	= between, among	**non-**	= not
con-	together	**intra-**	= within	**pre-**	= before
col-		**intro-**	= into	**sub-**	= under or below

Many prefixes, however, have more than one meaning. These prefixes also provide clues to the meanings of words:

PREFIXES HAVING MORE THAN ONE MEANING

ab-, a-	= not, away up, out	**re-**	= again back
dis-	= opposite of depriving of	**super-**	= over and above very large
in- (ir-, il-, im-)	= not in, into very	**trans-**	= across beyond
pro-	= in favor of forward ahead	**un-**	= not the opposite of

Using Prefixes and Base Words. Circle the prefix and underline the base word in each of the following words. Write the meaning of the prefix and of the complete word. Consult a dictionary if necessary.

1. subsurface _____

2. transmigrate _____

3. insincere _____

4. misrepresent _____

5. repossess _____

6. presuppose _____

7. malpractice _____

8. disassociate _____

9. prolabor _____

10. conform _____

Suffixes (I)

A **suffix** is a word part that is added to the end of another word or word part.

BASE WORD	SUFFIX	NEW WORD
scholar +	-ship =	scholarship
manage +	-ment =	management
sad +	-ness =	sadness

A **noun suffix** forms a noun when it is added to another word or word part. Learning common noun suffixes can increase your ability to recognize the meanings of unfamiliar words.

NOUN SUFFIXES THAT MEAN "ONE WHO DOES SOMETHING"

-ant	accountant	**-er**	stenographer	**-ian**	physician
-eer	electioneer	**-ist**	typist	**-or**	inventor

NOUN SUFFIXES THAT MAKE ABSTRACT WORDS

-ance, -ence	reluctance, dependence	**-ment**	improvement
-ation, -tion	determination, correction	**-ness**	shyness
-dom	freedom	**-ship**	authorship
-hood	childhood	**-tude**	solitude
-ice	cowardice	**-ty, -ity**	loyalty, equality
-ism	socialism		

Using Suffixes To Determine Meaning. Circle the suffix and underline the base word in each of the following words. Write the meaning of the suffix and of the whole word. Consult a dictionary if necessary.

1. nationalism _____

2. embarrassment _____

3. stillness _____

4. engineer _____

5. physicist _____

6. alteration _____

7. possibility _____

8. justice _____

9. clinician _____

10. novelty _____

Using Suffixes To Form New Words. Add a noun suffix to each of the words below.

1. patriot _____   5. legal _____

2. type _____   6. occupy _____

3. lazy _____   7. beauty _____

4. special _____   8. note _____

Suffixes (II)

An **adjective suffix** is a suffix that is used to form an adjective.

ADJECTIVE SUFFIXES THAT MEAN "FULL OF"

-ous	hazardous	**-acious**	sagacious
-ose	grandiose	**-ful**	painful

ADJECTIVE SUFFIXES THAT MEAN "RELATING TO" OR "PERTAINING TO"

-al	lyrical	**-ical**	philosophical
-ant	defiant	**-ish**	fiendish
-ic	Arabic	**-ive, -ative**	creative, talkative

ADJECTIVE SUFFIXES THAT MEAN WHAT THEY SAY

-able, -ible	comfortable, sensible	**-less**	tasteless
-most	innermost	**-like**	childlike

Using Suffixes To Determine Meaning. Circle the suffix and underline the base word in each of the following words. Write the meaning of the suffix and of the whole word. Consult a dictionary if necessary.

1. glorious _____

2. comatose _____

3. structural _____

4. restful _____

5. original _____

6. volcanic _____

7. theatrical _____

8. dangerous _____

9. feverish _____

10. destructive _____

11. receivable _____

12. bottommost _____

13. flexible _____

14. timeless _____

15. homelike _____

Using Suffixes To Form New Words. Add an adjective suffix to each of the words below.

1. beauty _____   4. peril _____

2. defect _____   5. mystery _____

3. valor _____   6. architecture _____

Roots

A **root** is a word part to which a prefix or a suffix may be added. Each of the following roots is used in a whole family of English words. If you know the meanings of these roots, you will be able to determine the basic meaning of many new words.

USEFUL GREEK ROOTS			USEFUL LATIN ROOTS		
anthrop	=	human	**capt**	=	take, hold, seize
aster, astr	=	star	**cede, cess**	=	yield, give away
auto	=	self, alone	**cred**	=	believe
bibl	=	book	**dic, dict**	=	speak, say
bi, bio	=	life	**duc, duct**	=	lead
crac, crat	=	govern	**fac, fec**	=	do, make
dem	=	people	**mit, miss**	=	send
geo	=	earth	**pon, pos, posit**	=	place, put
graph	=	write	**port**	=	carry
gram	=	write	**scrib, script**	=	write
log	=	word, reason	**spec**	=	look, see
logy	=	study of	**stat**	=	stand, put in place
metr, meter	=	measure	**vers, vert**	=	turn
nom, nym	=	name, word, law	**vid, vis**	=	see
phil	=	love	**voc, vok**	=	call
soph	=	wise, wisdom	**vol**	=	wish

Using Roots To Determine Meaning. Define each of the following words. Consult a dictionary if necessary.

1. access _____

2. credibility _____

3. autohypnosis _____

4. prediction _____

5. deduction _____

6. monogram _____

7. remission _____

8. facility _____

9. biochemical _____

10. sociology _____

11. scribble _____

12. astrophotography _____

13. stationary _____

14. metrical _____

15. visor _____

16. portable _____

Word Families

A **word family** is a group of words that have a common root. As you have learned, the Latin root *voc* or *vok* means "call." Many English words contain this root: *voc*al, *voc*alize, e*voke*, *voc*ation. Many additional words that contain this root have prefixes added in front of the root: pro*voke*, re*voke*, in*voke*. Still other words that contain this root have both prefixes and suffixes: in*voc*ation, sub*voc*alize, pro*voc*ation. Being able to identify the root in a longer word will help you unlock its meaning.

Identifying Word Families. Identify the root in each group of words below. Give its basic meaning. Be sure you can define each of the words in the "family."

1. grammar, telegram, program, anagram, epigram

_____

2. credit, incredible, discredit, credibility, credence

_____

3. geography, geology, geometry, geode

_____

4. vision, televise, revise, visible, visit

_____

5. station, statue, status, stationary, thermostat

_____

6. disaster, asterisk, aster, asteroid, astronomy

_____

7. bibliography, bibliophile, Bible, bibliomania

_____

8. dictate, prediction, benediction, dictaphone, malediction

_____

Working with Word Families. Under each word below, write three words that contain the same root. Begin by underlining the root.

1. respect   2. graphic   3. admit

_____   _____   _____

_____   _____   _____

_____   _____   _____

Review: Building Your Vocabulary

Using Context Clues and Inference. Circle the word that is closest in meaning to the italicized word.

1. The bird's nest was safely hidden behind the dense *foliage* of the tree.

   a. shade   b. flowers   c. leaves   d. trunk

2. Since Mr. Downing was in a hurry for the material, he found it *expedient* to carry the fabric home rather than to have it sent.

   a. heavy   b. convenient   c. expensive   d. awkward

3. Marmosets are *arboreal* creatures; they spend their lives scampering about in trees.

   a. interesting   b. talkative   c. tree-dwelling   d. tiny

4. From the *lugubrious* expressions of the people coming out of the theater, I could tell that the movie had a tragic ending.

   a. fierce   b. happy   c. very sad   d. excited

5. The students at the conservatory often paint *facsimilies* of works by the old masters. This week, for example, they are trying to reproduce Rembrandt's *The Night Watch*.

   a. posters   b. copies   c. errors   d. perspectives

6. You must overcome your *lassitude* and start getting things accomplished once again.

   a. fright   b. listlessness   c. excitement   d. thoughtfulness

Using Word Parts. Each of the italicized words in the sentences below contains two or more word parts. Draw lines between the parts of the italicized word in each sentence. Then, based on the meanings of these word parts, write a definition of the italicized word.

   EXAMPLE: un|imagin|able—not capable of being imagined

1. The errors in the broadcaster's report were *inexcusable*.

_____

2. The doctors acted on the *presupposition* that the disease was contagious.

_____

3. The device that sends out radio signals is called a *transmitter*.

_____

4. The passengers were ready to *disembark*.

_____

5. The speech class is studying *interpersonal* communication.

_____

6. Martin had very little *recollection* of his dreams.

_____

What's in a Dictionary Entry?

Dictionary entries contain some or all of the following parts: the *entry*, or word being defined; the *pronunciation*; the *part of speech* abbreviation; the *etymology*, or history of the word; and the *definition*. In addition, many entries include a list of *synonyms*, a list of *antonyms*, *derived words*, and *cross references*.

PRONUNCIATION ——————————

ENTRY WORD ——————————

CROSS REFERENCE ——————————

PART OF SPEECH

ETYMOLOGY

DEFINITIONS

DERIVED WORD

SYNONYMS

ANTONYMS

al·le·giance (ə lē′jəns) *n.* [< OFr. *a-*, to + *ligeance* < *liege:* see LIEGE] **1.** the obligation to support and be loyal to one's ruler or country **2.** loyalty or devotion, as to a cause, person, etc. —**al·le′giant** (-jənt) *adj., n.*
SYN.—**allegiance** refers to a citizen's duty to his government or a similar obligation to support a cause, leader, etc.; **fidelity** suggests strong faithfulness to an obligation, trust, etc.; **loyalty** suggests a firm and unquestioning devotion that one may feel for one's family, friends, or country; **fealty**, now chiefly a literary word, suggests faithfulness that one has sworn to uphold, as that of a vassal to his lord —**ANT.** faithlessness, disaffection

Understanding Dictionary Entries. Study the sample entry for the word *allegiance*. Fill in the blanks using information provided in the entry.

1. One synonym for *allegiance* is _____.

2. *Allegiance* has _____ different definitions.

3. *Allegiance* is divided into _____ syllables.

4. _____ is a derived word made by changing the suffix of the

word *allegiance* to *-ant*.

5. The note *see LIEGE* in the etymology, is an example of a _____

6. Two antonyms (*ANT.*) for *allegiance* are _____ and _____

7. According to the etymology, the word *allegiance* contains the Old French prefix

a, which means _____.

8. The word *allegiance* is a _____. (part of speech)

9. The word *allegiance* is accented on the _____ syllable.

10. The word *allegiant* is both an _____ and a _____

(parts of speech)

The Multiple Meanings of Words

Many of the words listed in dictionaries have more than one meaning. A good way to develop your vocabulary is to learn additional meanings for words that you already know.

Working with Multiple Meanings. The word *rake* is used in several different ways in the sentences below. On the blank after each sentence, define the word *rake* as it is used in that particular sentence. Consult a dictionary if necessary.

1. The gardener left his *rake* on the courthouse lawn.

_____

2. Ms. Russo expects her new video equipment shop to *rake* in a lot of money.

_____

3. The reporter *raked* up facts that had been hidden for years.

_____

4. *Rake* the fire carefully before you leave the campsite.

_____

5. The troopers *raked* the countryside looking for the lost child.

_____

Using Words with Multiple Meanings. The word *fine* has many different meanings. Consult a dictionary and find five meanings for the word. Write a sentence for each of the separate meanings. Each sentence should clearly illustrate the meaning of the word.

1. _____

2. _____

3. _____

4. _____

5. _____

Finding Multiple Meanings in the Dictionary. Look through the dictionary and locate two words with multiple meanings. Write the words and two of their meanings below.

Word 1 _____   Word 2 _____

1. _____   1. _____

_____   _____

2. _____   2. _____

_____   _____

Synonyms and Antonyms

One way to sharpen your vocabulary is by using synonyms and antonyms. **Synonyms** are words that have similar meanings. **Antonyms** are words that have opposite meanings.

Determining Shades of Meaning Among Synonyms. Each of the following words shares the general meaning of "a person in opposition to another," yet each word has a more exact meaning. Give a specific definition of each.

1. enemy _____

2. opponent _____

3. competitor _____

4. rival _____

5. antagonist _____

Using Synonyms and Antonyms. For each word below, list one synonym and one antonym. Use each word in a sentence that illustrates the exact meaning of the word.

begin   SYN: _____   ANT: _____

1. _____

2. _____

3. _____

happiness   SYN: _____   ANT: _____

1. _____

2. _____

3. _____

warm   SYN: _____   ANT: _____

1. _____

2. _____

3. _____

quiet   SYN: _____   ANT: _____

1. _____

2. _____

3. _____

Interesting Word Origins

Many English words have unusual histories. Some come from languages very different from English. The word *algebra*, for example, comes from Arabic words meaning "the reunion of broken parts."

Other familiar English words were originally the names of people or of literary characters. A task that requires great strength, for instance, is sometimes called *herculean*. Hercules was a legendary Greek hero who performed many difficult labors.

Understanding Word Origins. Write a definition for each of the following words. Then, on the second line, explain the origin of the word. Use a dictionary as necessary.

1. jersey _____

_____

2. jovial _____

_____

3. panic _____

_____

4. hamburger _____

_____

5. Wednesday _____

_____

6. alphabet _____

_____

7. odyssey _____

_____

8. robot _____

_____

9. jeep _____

_____

10. sarcasm _____

_____

11. lyric _____

_____

12. humor _____

_____

Review: Using the Dictionary

Obtaining Information from Dictionary Entries. Use a dictionary to find the information requested below.

1. Tell what part of speech the word *impute* belongs to. _____

2. Give two definitions for the word *liable*. _____

_____

_____

3. Write the pronunciation of the word *integral*. Tell which syllable the accent falls on.

_____

_____

4. Find two synonyms for the word *mirth*. Use each in a sentence.

_____

_____

_____

_____

5. Give the etymology of the word *martial*. _____

_____

Working with Multiple Meanings. The word *stand* has many meanings. Find four different meanings for the word. Write a sentence that illustrates each specific meaning.

1. _____

2. _____

3. _____

4. _____

Working with Synonyms and Antonyms. Using a dictionary, complete this chart.

	Word	Synonym	Antonym
1.	gaunt		stout
2.	decline	refuse	
3.	chide	rebuke	
4.	confirm		disprove

Terms from Specialized Areas

Words that are part of the special vocabulary of a technical or professional field often find their way into everyday English. In sports, for example, *fencing* means "dueling with swords." However, this word can also be used to describe dueling with words. The following are some other common words that come from specialized areas:

SPORTS	THE ARTS	THE MASS MEDIA
par	mime	sound effect
jockey	chorus	layout
hurdle	myth	rerun

BUSINESS	SCIENCE	COMPUTER SCIENCE
inventory	paranoid	format
bottom line	momentum	glitch
wholesale	light-years	networking

Using Terms from Specialized Areas. Fill in the blanks in the following sentences with words from the lists provided above. Use a dictionary as necessary.

1. A _____ of "thank you's" greeted Mr. Garcia's announcement that we would have an extra day to finish the report.

2. Michael took _____ of the food in the pantry.

3. We have conquered smallpox. The next _____ is cancer.

4. Ms. Plessas found her new job in marketing by _____ with other businesswomen whom she met at conferences.

5. The firefighters managed to prevent the _____ destruction of the forest by cutting down trees in the path of the fire.

6. Some investigators think that the lost city of Atlantis is just a _____.

7. The two countries remain _____ apart on several key issues.

8. The only _____ in the Student Council's plan to purchase a new electronic scoreboard is that the money is not yet available.

9. Ms. Clark didn't like the new _____ of the office.

10. Winning six games in a row has given the team enough _____ to sweep the playoffs.

11. I became _____ about amusement park rides after the accident.

12. Cora's playing is on a _____ with that of a professional oboist.

13. Supper will be a _____ of last night's since no one will have time to do much cooking.

14. My influence on Sheila has been extensive; sometimes she will even

_____ my gestures and expressions.

The Levels of Language

Standard English is language that follows the rules of good grammar, usage, and mechanics. Almost all audiences and occasions call for standard English. There are two kinds of standard English: formal and informal. **Formal English** is language that is appropriate for serious or ceremonial occasions. **Informal English** is language that is suited to everyday speech and writing.

Nonstandard English is language that does not follow the rules of good grammar, usage, and mechanics. It is not acceptable in most situations. Two types of nonstandard English are slang and gobbledygook. **Slang** is made up of popular, faddish words and phrases. **Gobbledygook** is complicated language that contains long sentences and unfamiliar or awkward words and phrases. Often, gobbledygook contains jargon as well. **Jargon** is language used to describe specialized activities. Avoid slang and gobbledygook in your speech and writing. Use jargon only when your audience will understand it.

Avoiding Slang, Jargon, and Gobbledygook. The following sentences contain examples of slang, jargon, and gobbledygook. Rewrite these sentences using simple, direct standard English. Consult a dictionary as necessary.

1. Marsha wants to be a hoofer in a Broadway musical. _____

_____

2. The maximization of one's individual competency in orthographic endeavors ought

to be a prominent objective. _____

_____

3. The use of tobacco-related products is a major factor in the etiology of several

pulmonary diseases. _____

_____

4. The detective was a tough cookie. _____

_____

5. Laura plays a mean guitar. _____

_____

Using Appropriate Language. The following paragraph from a report contains a mixture of types of English. On your own paper, rewrite the paragraph using only formal English.

What occupations did the Presidents of the United States pursue before they were elected to office? Well, they did lots of different types of stuff. A big bunch of them— over half, in fact—were attorneys. Four were military guys. Three ran farms or plantations. Other Presidents have been teachers, businessmen, authors, engineers, and editors. We've even had one tailor and one actor. It just goes to show you: people from all kinds of backgrounds and things can grow up to become President. If you ask me, that's really kind of neat.

Joining Sentences and Sentence Parts

Sentences that state ideas of equal importance can be joined with **, and**, **, but**, or **, or**.

> The official name of India is *Bharat*. Its capital is New Delhi.
> The official name of India is *Bharat*, **and** its capital is New Delhi.

Sentence parts of equal importance can often be joined with **and**, **but**, or **or**. When sentence parts are joined, no comma is used, and repeated words, such as those shown in italics below, are deleted.

> Sue Halpern won a Rhodes Scholarship. *Sue Halpern* studied at Oxford University.
> Sue Halpern won a Rhodes Scholarship **and** studied at Oxford University.

Joining Sentences and Sentence Parts. Join each pair of sentences by following the directions in parentheses. Eliminate the italicized words.

1. The team captain was thrown out of the game. We won anyway. (Join with **, but**.)

_____

2. The divers found the sunken ship. *The divers* recovered its cargo. (Join with **and**.)

_____

3. Did Edison invent motion pictures? Did he simply contribute to their development? (Join with **, or**.)

_____

4. Caecilians look like worms. *Caecilians* are actually amphibians. (Join with **but**.)

_____

5. Have you seen the Grand Tetons? *Have you seen* the Badlands? (Join with **or**.)

_____

6. Catfish have taste buds in their skin. The tongues of lizards are used to touch and smell. (Join with **, and**.)

_____

7. Lee loves watching television. He hates situation comedies. (Join with **, but**.)

_____

8. We can drive around Lake Michigan. *We can* take the ferry across. (Join with **or**.)

_____

9. Seals live in Antarctica. Penguins *live in Antarctica*. (Join with **and**.)

_____

10. Will the test be short? Will it take the entire class period? (Join with **, or**.)

_____

Adding Words and Groups of Words

Sometimes you can combine sentences by adding single words or groups of words.

"The Lie" is a short story. *The story is* interesting.
"The Lie" is an interesting short story.

The books are from the library. *The books are* lying on my desk.
The books lying on my desk are from the library.

Occasionally, you must change the ending of an added word to **-ing**, **-ed**, or **-ly**.

Review your notes before the exam. *Your review should be* thorough.
Review your notes thoroughly before the exam.

We saw a horse. *The horse* galloped across the open field.
We saw a horse galloping across the open field.

Sometimes you will have to separate the added words with commas.

Rosalyn Yalow won the Nobel Prize in Medicine. *Rosalyn Yalow is* a nuclear physicist.
Rosalyn Yalow, a nuclear physicist, won the Nobel Prize in Medicine.

Adding Words and Groups of Words. Combine the following pairs of sentences. Eliminate the italicized words, and follow any directions given in parentheses.

1. The deer on the road was startled by the lights. *The lights* glowed. (End the added word with **-ing**.)

_____

2. The villagers wouldn't go near the house. *The house was* at the top of the hill.

_____

3. Ireland is called "Eire" in Gaelic. *Gaelic is* the ancient language of Ireland. (Use a comma.)

_____

4. The octopus sprayed a substance at its foe. *The substance was* inky.

_____

5. Ann Colman sang. *Her singing was* beautiful. (End the important word with **-ly**.)

_____

6. Did you see the children? *They* splashed around in the water. (Change the ending of *splashed* to **-ing**.)

_____

7. Our front yard is full of roses and asters. *The roses and asters are* in full bloom.

_____

8. I go on several hiking trips every summer. *The trips are* long.

_____

Combining with *Who*, *Which*, and *That*

Often, when you add a group of words to a sentence, you will have to begin the added group of words with *who*, *which*, or *that*.

If a group of words refers to a person and is necessary to the meaning of the combined sentence, join with *who*.

> The creature was spotted by a villager. *The villager* lives near Loch Ness.
> The creature was spotted by a villager **who** lives near Loch Ness.

If a group of words refers to a person and is not necessary to the meaning of the combined sentence, join with *who*. Separate the added words with commas.

> Joan Benoit won the Olympic marathon. *Joan Benoit* lives in Maine.
> Joan Benoit**, who** lives in Maine**,** won the Olympic marathon.

If a group of words refers to a thing and is necessary to the meaning of the combined sentence, join with *that*.

> Krill are tiny crustaceans. *Krill* are harvested for food.
> Krill are tiny crustaceans **that** are harvested for food.

If a group of words refers to a thing and is not necessary to the meaning of the combined sentence, join with *which*. Separate the added words with commas.

> For dinner we had kohlrabi. *Kohlrabi* is a vegetable related to the cabbage.
> For dinner we had kohlrabi**, which** is a vegetable related to the cabbage.

Joining with *Who*, *Which*, and *That*. Combine each pair of sentences, following the directions given in parentheses. Eliminate the italicized words.

1. A cat's whiskers help the animal to feel its way in the dark. *A cat's whiskers* are very sensitive. (Join with **which**. Use a pair of commas.)

_____

2. Colette asked for my recipe for rice pudding. *Colette* almost never cooks. (Join with **who**. Use a pair of commas.)

_____

3. The picture is of my Aunt Alma. *The picture* hangs over the fireplace. (Join with **that**.)

_____

4. The journalist was Dan Rather. *The journalist* reported the story. (Join with **who**.)

_____

5. The Pittman General Store is over one hundred years old. The Pittman General Store is now being torn down. (Join with **which**. Use a pair of commas.)

_____

6. Ms. Palmer went with us on the field trip. *Ms. Palmer* teaches American history. (Join with **who**. Use a pair of commas.)

_____

Combining Sentences Using Substitution

Read the following pair of sentences.

Janet plays soccer. *This* is Janet's favorite pastime.

Notice that *this* in the second sentence refers to the entire idea in the first sentence. This pair of sentences, and others like it, can be combined into a single statement.

Playing soccer is Janet's favorite pastime.

The word *plays* was changed to *playing*, and the italicized words were eliminated.

Combining with -*ing*. Combine each group of sentences by using **-ing**. Eliminate the italicized words.

1. *We* won the playoff game. *This* made us extremely happy.

_____

2. *I* read a book on the Mayans. *This* led me to become interested in archaeology.

_____

3. *Erica wanted to* speak fluent German. *That* was Erica's goal.

_____

4. *The director* filmed inside the mouth of the volcano. *That* was difficult.

_____

5. *My cat* sleeps. *That* is my cat's primary occupation.

_____

6. *David Livingstone* explored south-central Africa. *That* was David Livingstone's major accomplishment.

_____

7. *Sandy* stood on the deck of the ship. *This* caused Sandy to become seasick.

_____

8. *A writer must* have a vivid imagination. *That* is essential to becoming a writer.

_____

9. *Jackie* practices daily. *That* is a key to Jackie's success.

_____

10. *Susan* started to write her essay at 11 P.M. *That* didn't give Susan enough time to do a good job.

_____

_____

Combining To Show Causes and Effects

Read the following sentences.

> The battery was dead. The car wouldn't start.

The first sentence in this pair states a cause. The second sentence states an effect. You can combine such sentences by placing *because*, *since*, or *for* before the cause.

> The car wouldn't start **because** the battery was dead.

You can also place a comma and *so* before the effect.

> The battery was dead, **so** the car wouldn't start.

Yet another way to join such sentences is to place *therefore*, *as a result*, *consequently*, or *thus* before the effect. If you join two sentences using one of these words, place a semicolon before the word and a comma after it.

> The battery was dead; **therefore,** the car wouldn't start.

Joining Sentences To Show Causes and Effects. Combine each pair of sentences, following the directions given in parentheses.

1.   Moviegoers are demanding more realism. Many movies are now being made on location. (Combine with **; as a result**.)

_____

2.   I am going to summer school to take typing. I should be able to work part time in the office this fall. (Combine with **; therefore**.)

_____

3.   We had to pile our books on the floor. The bookcases were already full. (Combine with **for**.)

_____

4.   Helium-filled balloons rise. They are lighter than air. (Combine with **because**.)

_____

5.   The concert is sold out. We will have to go to a movie. (Combine with **, so**.)

_____

6.   Some mosquitoes live in the tops of trees. Biologists have to build treehouses in order to study them. (Combine with **since**.)

_____

7.   The doctor can't be in her office this afternoon. Cancel her appointments. (Combine with **; therefore**.)

_____

8.   The clock has stopped. The electricity went off. (Combine with **because**.)

_____

Avoiding Empty Sentences

Sentences that say too little are **empty sentences.** Grammatically they may be complete; however, they are lacking in ideas. To improve empty sentences, you may have to provide additional information.

EMPTY: I was unhappy at summer camp because I didn't like it there.
IMPROVED: I was unhappy at summer camp because I was lonely and bored.

Another way to improve an empty sentence is to shorten it.

EMPTY: Meryl Streep should win the Oscar for best actress this season because she is the season's best actress.
IMPROVED: Meryl Streep should win the Oscar for best actress this season.

Revising Empty Sentences. Rewrite the following empty sentences.

1. Our team won the game by scoring more baskets than our opponents scored.

_____

2. The roads are more crowded at rush hour because there are more cars on them during that busy period. _____

_____

3. I didn't make it to class on time because I was late. _____

_____

4. Medicine has made progress against several degenerative diseases that gradually get worse. _____

_____

5. Having finished the test, I checked the questions I had finished to see if I had finished everything. _____

_____

6. Weekly news magazines, if you read them every week, are a good way of keeping up with the news that happened during the week. _____

_____

7. I don't type well, and I don't have good handwriting, but my typing is not good.

_____

8. The roads were impassable because of the rain, and no one could get through.

_____

Avoiding Padded Sentences

Padded sentences are sentences that contain unnecessary words. Such sentences are ineffective and lacking in force.

Padding can result from the following:

    repetition of the same word or idea
    repetition of *that*
    use of fillers such as "on account of . . .," "the reason is that . . .,"
        "what I believe is . . .," "the thing . . ."

To revise padded sentences, omit the unnecessary words.

PADDED: What I think is that we need a new public address system.
BETTER: We need a new public address system.

Revising Padded Sentences. Revise the following sentences.

1. Today, many modern cities are more advanced than those of yesterday. _____

_____

2. In my opinion, I think bicycling is the best exercise in the world. _____

_____

3. The thing I am concerned about most is air pollution. _____

_____

4. On account of the fact that it rained, our plans for a field trip were canceled. _____

_____

5. It is important that since they don't like chili that we not serve it. _____

_____

6. The reason that I didn't get a ten-speed bike was that a ten-speed was not the type

of bike that I wanted. _____

_____

7. When we had our garage sale, it was on account of the fact that we had too much

junk in the garage. _____

_____

8. I don't know for sure, and I may be wrong, but I think I saw a dog coming

out of the henhouse. _____

_____

Avoiding Overloaded Sentences

IMPROVING YOUR SENTENCES 23

Overloaded sentences are sentences that say too much. They carry too many ideas. They mix up important ideas with unimportant ones. In order to avoid overloaded sentences, you should

1. First, decide on the main ideas.
2. Decide which ideas can be combined into one sentence.
3. Write the main idea as one sentence, following the usual sentence pattern of subject—verb—object.
4. Write separate sentences for the other ideas.
5. Write simply and clearly.

OVERLOADED: I want to be a teacher and work with young people, and I think that teaching is a rewarding profession.

REVISED: I want to be a teacher and work with young people. Teaching, after all, is a rewarding profession.

Revising Overloaded Sentences. Revise each of the following sentences.

1. Michael earned extra money by repairing lawn mowers and snow blowers, and he saved two hundred dollars, which was enough money to buy a guitar. _____

_____

_____

2. In French class we are learning French grammar, and French grammar is much like English grammar, which I know pretty well. _____

_____

3. We are going to Disney World for vacation and will also visit our grandparents in St. Petersburg, which is a historic old city that we learned about in seventh grade.

_____

_____

4. Psychology is a fairly new science, and its principles are still being discovered, and because there is the possibility of making important new discoveries, psychology is exciting. _____

_____

5. There was a heavy downpour, and the river rose, causing the engineers who work at the Misandwee Dam to worry that the dam, which is quite old, might burst.

_____

_____

Keeping to the Point

Omit irrelevant details that interrupt the meaning of a sentence.

IRRELEVANT DETAILS: Our math teacher, who is the youngest of five children in her family, gave us a long homework assignment.

IMPROVED: Our math teacher gave us a long homework assignment.

Keeping to the Point. Revise the following sentences.

1. The library book that I am reading, which I thought I lost one day, is a biography of Helen Keller. _____

_____

2. Lunar eclipses occur when the moon, which is beautiful when it is full, passes through the shadow of the earth. _____

_____

3. Mary Cassatt was one of the greatest painters in the history of American art, and I like to paint, too. _____

_____

4. The candidate, who resembles my Uncle Bill, spoke knowledgeably about important issues of the campaign. _____

_____

5. Thomas Jefferson, who studied Old English, was President from 1801 to 1809.

_____

6. Our car, which has denim upholstery, was damaged by a hit-and-run driver.

_____

7. Dad was upset about how high our telephone bill was, since it contained several long-distance calls, and I had charged a pair of shoes without asking him. _____

_____

_____

8. Walking catfish have lunglike organs that enable them to stay out of water for long periods of time, and catfish are good to eat. _____

_____

Keeping Related Parts Together

Keep related sentence parts close together. Avoid separating them with other words.

AWKWARD: I am, when I finish eating this ice cream, going for a bike ride. (Parts of the verb are separated.)

BETTER: When I finish eating this ice cream, I am going for a bike ride.

AWKWARD: Debbie, after getting her ears pierced, bought some earrings. (Subject and verb are separated.)

BETTER: After getting her ears pierced, Debbie bought some earrings.

AWKWARD: I bought, when I was downtown, new gym shoes. (Verb and object are separated.)

BETTER: I bought new gym shoes when I was downtown.

Keeping Related Parts Together. Revise each sentence below as necessary.

1. Our car was, while parked on the street, sideswiped. _____

   _____

2. I was reading, while relaxing on the sofa, a new book by Judy Blume. _____

   _____

3. Julie, while drinking a glass of iced tea, finished her homework. _____

   _____

4. Dad is, whenever someone leaves a bike in the driveway, really annoyed. _____

   _____

5. I watched, a few weeks ago, a television documentary about special effects in films. _____

   _____

6. Joey is enjoying, now that he is in fourth grade, his schoolwork more than ever. _____

   _____

7. Bob, while playing his electric guitar, was keeping the whole family awake. _____

   _____

8. There are, according to the rules of baseball, nine players on a team. _____

   _____

9. The baboon gave, when the lion approached, a warning signal. _____

   _____

10. The pianist had, because his eyesight was failing, to wear special glasses. _____

   _____

Avoiding Overuse of *and*

Although *and* is a useful conjunction for joining ideas, its overuse creates a decidedly uninteresting style. Avoid stringing together a series of ideas with *and's*. One way to avoid overuse of *and* is to write separate sentences. Another way is to replace *and's* with linking words that show how your ideas are related.

AWKWARD: I like ice cream, and I am not supposed to eat foods high in butterfat.

IMPROVED: I like ice cream; *however,* I am not supposed to eat foods high in butterfat.

The following linking words are often used to show how ideas are related:

consequently	also	at the same time	however
hence	besides	on the other hand	nonetheless
therefore	likewise	otherwise	still

Using Linking Words. The following sentences are loosely strung together with *and's*. Revise these sentences, using linking words to show how the ideas are related.

1. I am studying typing, and I should be able to work in an office next fall.

_____

2. The train was scheduled to arrive at 6:30, and by 7:00 it had not arrived.

_____

3. One of the computers on the shuttle failed, and the flight still took place.

_____

4. The branches are touching the power lines, and the tree must be trimmed.

_____

5. You must wear a life jacket when rowing, and you might drown if the boat overturns.

_____

6. Vitamins are good for you, and taking too many can be dangerous. _____

_____

7. Megan is taking driver's education, and her car insurance will be lower.

_____

8. Most people thought that the commercial was irritating, and the company continued

to air the commercial anyway. _____

_____

Subordinating Ideas Correctly

Another way to join ideas effectively is to write complex sentences. In such sentences, the main idea is expressed in the main clause and the less important idea in the subordinate clause.

SUBORDINATE IDEA	MAIN IDEA

After we had been swimming,   we stayed in the shade to avoid sunburn.

When subordinating ideas, avoid the errors of faulty coordination and faulty subordination. **Faulty coordination** occurs when the writer joins two ideas that obviously are not of equal value and cannot be joined by *and*. Faulty coordination can be corrected by changing one of the clauses into a subordinate clause, a phrase, or an appositive.

FAULTY: I spent three hours cleaning my room, and Mom said it looked nice.
REVISED: After I spent three hours cleaning my room, Mom said it looked nice.

Faulty subordination occurs when the writer states the main idea in a subordinate clause.

FAULTY: Jerry was reading the newspaper while he kept falling asleep.
REVISED: While he was reading the newspaper, Jerry kept falling asleep.

Coordinating and Subordinating Ideas. Revise the sentences below to correct mistakes in faulty coordination and subordination.

1.   Since Melinda is studying tonight, she has a chemistry test tomorrow. _____

_____

2.   Because I am putting my allowance in the bank, I have to pay for the window I broke

while playing softball. _____

_____

3.   We went on vacation and our neighbor kept our parakeets. _____

_____

4.   I fell off my skateboard, and my ankle was broken in two places. _____

_____

5.   Our house is getting too small for us, and we saw a real estate agent about trying to

sell it this spring. _____

_____

6.   It rained steadily for an hour, and the officials decided to postpone the game. _____

_____

_____

Making Sentence Parts Parallel

The coordinating conjunction *and* joins sentence parts of equal value: noun and noun, verb and verb, phrase and phrase, clause and clause. The constructions are then **parallel.** If *and* is used to join constructions of different kinds, there is a lack of parallelism.

FAULTY: Sandra enjoys *hiking* and *to go camping.* (gerund and infinitive phrase)
REVISED: Sandra enjoys *hiking* and *camping.* (gerund and gerund)
FAULTY: The fruit salad contained *apples, oranges,* and *there were bananas in it.* (two nouns and a clause)
REVISED: The fruit salad contained *apples, oranges,* and *bananas.* (three nouns)

Lack of parallelism often occurs when the pronouns *which* and *who* are used in a sentence.

FAULTY: Mr. Scarlotti is my *neighbor* and *who has a beautiful flower garden each year.* (noun and clause)
REVISED: *Mr. Scarlotti is my neighbor,* and *he has a beautiful flower garden each year.* (clause and clause)
SIMPLER: Mr. Scarlotti, my neighbor, has a beautiful flower garden each year.

Parallelism. Revise these sentences to make the constructions parallel.

1. I practiced playing the piano and how to read symphonic scores. _____

_____

2. We listened to the radio and which broadcast an interesting interview. _____

_____

3. The reading room in the rare book library was large, luxurious, and nice furnishings.

_____

4. The lottery was won by a truck driver and who says he will quit his job now. _____

_____

5. At camp we learned horseback riding, water skiing, and to pitch a tent. _____

_____

6. That dog's favorite activities were chewing on slippers and it chased cars. _____

_____

7. My typewriter is old and which needs some repair. _____

_____

8. We planned to shop all afternoon and eating in a nice restaurant. _____

_____

Improve the following sentences by

Avoiding empty sentences	Keeping related sentence parts together
Avoiding padded sentences	Avoiding overuse of *and*
Avoiding overloaded sentences	Subordinating ideas correctly
Keeping to the point	Making sentence parts parallel

1. It is my opinion that people can conserve energy, and that they should use less fuel and electricity. _____

_____

2. The overheated car was, though it was still running, steaming and hissing. _____

_____

_____

3. The beans we grew are ready to pick, and I will pick them now. _____

_____

_____

4. The auto mechanic said we need new points and to put in a new oil filter. _____

_____

_____

5. The mayor spoke with the striking workers, and the mayor is young. _____

_____

_____

6. I didn't buy the expensive sweater because it cost too much. _____

_____

_____

7. The reason I went to bed early is that I am planning to get up before dawn on account of I plan to go fishing. _____

_____

_____

8. There was a bad accident, and I was hurt, and we missed the party. _____

_____

There are three stages in the **process of writing**: pre-writing, writing the first draft, and revising. In the **pre-writing** stage, you choose a topic, gather information, and organize your ideas. In the **writing** stage, you turn your ideas into sentences. In the **revising** stage, you look for ways to improve your content, organization, and language. Each of these stages is described in the chart below. Refer to this chart whenever you write.

The Process of Writing

Pre-Writing

1. Select a topic that interests you.
2. Narrow the topic until it can be thoroughly developed in the space available.
3. Identify your purpose.
4. Use your understanding of purpose and audience to determine your type of language and choice of details.
5. Gather and list details that you can use to develop your topic.
6. Evaluate and organize your list of details. Delete unrelated ideas. Add new ones. Put your details into a logical order.

Writing the First Draft

1. Keeping your audience and purpose in mind, begin to write.
2. Let your thoughts flow freely. Modify your initial plans for content and organization, if necessary. Do not be too concerned with grammar and mechanics at this point.

Revising

Read what you have written. Answer the following questions:

1. Did you stick to your topic?
2. Did you include everything you wanted to include?
3. Did you include any unnecessary or unrelated details?
4. Is each main idea clearly expressed and thoroughly developed?
5. Do tone, mood, and level of language remain consistent?
6. Do your ideas flow smoothly?
7. Is your writing organized logically, with a beginning, a middle, and an end? Are the ideas presented in an order that makes sense?
8. Is your writing interesting and lively? Is there variety in the length and structure of your sentences?
9. Is your word choice vivid and precise?
10. Do the language and the content suit your audience?
11. Have you accomplished your purpose?

Revise as necessary. Then proofread your work, using the checklist on page 31.

Guidelines for Proofreading

The final step in revising is **proofreading**. When you proofread, find and correct any errors you have made in grammar, usage, or mechanics. Always proofread your final drafts carefully. Refer to the following checklist to make sure that your proofreading is thorough.

Proofreading Checklist

Grammar and Usage

Are there any sentence fragments or run-ons?
Have you used verb tenses correctly?
Do all verbs agree with their subjects?
Have you used the correct form of each pronoun?
Have you used adjectives and adverbs correctly?
Are compound and complex sentences written and punctuated correctly?

Capitalization

Did you capitalize first words and all proper nouns and adjectives?
Are titles capitalized correctly?

Punctuation

Does each sentence have the proper end mark?
Are marks such as colons, semicolons, apostrophes, hyphens, and quotation marks used correctly?

Spelling

Are plurals and possessive forms spelled correctly?
Did you check all unfamiliar words in the dictionary?

Form

Were corrections made neatly?
In your final copy, is the writing legible?
Have you used the proper heading and margins?

Use these symbols when marking corrections on a final draft:

Proofreading Symbols

SYMBOL	MEANING	EXAMPLE
∧	insert	the key of A flat
≡	capitalize	halley's comet
/	make lower case	an Irish Setter
∩	transpose	thier beleifs
ℓ	delete	was firmly determined to
¶	make new paragraph	an end. A similar event
⌒	close up space	a world wide influence
⊙	insert period	at 1:30 P. M.
∧	add commas	lions, tigers, and bears

The Definition of a Paragraph

A **paragraph** is a group of closely related sentences dealing with a single subject. The **topic sentence** of a paragraph states the main idea. The other sentences develop and support the topic sentence. Many paragraphs also have a **concluding sentence** that summarizes the ideas expressed in the rest of the paragraph.

Two qualities of well-written paragraphs are unity and coherence. A paragraph has **unity** when all its sentences relate to the topic sentence. A paragraph has **coherence** when its sentences are arranged in a logical order and flow smoothly from idea to idea.

Revising for Unity and Coherence. Revise the following paragraph. Delete or replace sentences that do not relate to the idea expressed in the topic sentence. Rearrange the order of sentences as necessary to achieve coherence.

Though blind from birth, Genevieve Caulfield became one of the greatest educators and humanitarians the world has known. In 1923, she traveled to Japan, where she made a living teaching English and Braille. For information about publications in Braille, contact the American Foundation for the Blind in Washington, D.C. As a child, Genevieve taught herself to be completely independent. At the age of 17, she decided to devote her life to helping other blind people. Then, in 1938, she established the Bangkok School for the Blind in Thailand. Her efforts helped to improve the lives of blind people throughout the countries of Asia. In addition, she founded, in 1958, an elementary school for the blind in Saigon, Vietnam. Mary Eliza McDowell was another great humanitarian.

A **topic sentence** states the main idea of a paragraph. A good topic sentence meets the following requirements:

1. **It presents a general statement.** A topic sentence must be broad enough to introduce all the ideas in the rest of the paragraph.

2. **It limits the scope of the paragraph.** A topic sentence must be narrow enough to be developed completely by the rest of the paragraph.

Writing Topic Sentences. The following paragraphs have poor topic sentences. Tell what is wrong with each topic sentence by circling **a**, for "too broad," or **b**, for "too narrow." Then, write a good topic sentence for each paragraph.

1. American history is fascinating. Both Lincoln and Kennedy served their terms with Vice-Presidents named Johnson. Lincoln was elected to office in 1860; Kennedy was elected in 1960. Lincoln's secretary was named Kennedy; Kennedy's secretary was named Lincoln. Each President's last name contained seven letters. Both were assassinated while serving their terms of office. Though these similarities are only coincidences, they are nonetheless thought-provoking.

Old Topic Sentence (circle one):   a. too broad   b. too narrow

New Topic Sentence: _____

2. One important part of the modern symphony orchestra is the string section. The strings include violins, violas, cellos, and basses. In the woodwind section, there are flutes, oboes, clarinets, bassoons, English horns, and piccolos. The brass section contains French horns, trumpets, trombones, and tubas. The percussion section includes drums, cymbals, a tambourine, a triangle, and bells.

Old Topic Sentence (circle one):   a. too broad   b. too narrow

New Topic Sentence: _____

3. Omar Khayyám, the Persian poet of the eleventh century, made one great contribution to the literature of the world. He wrote a famous series of verses called *The Rubaiyat*. In addition, he made astronomical observations that enabled him to produce an extremely accurate calendar. He also wrote a book on algebra that is considered a landmark in the history of mathematics.

Old Topic Sentence (circle one):   a. too broad   b. too narrow

New Topic Sentence: _____

4. Mountain climbing is exciting and challenging. The following equipment is used in rock climbing: ropes, pitons, snap links, and chocks. Pitons are iron spikes that can be hammered into cracks and crevices. A piton has a ring on one end to which a rope can be tied. Snap links are clips used to attach ropes to climbers or to pitons. Chocks are metal nuts that can be inserted into cracks and attached to slings. They are often used instead of pitons.

Old Topic Sentence (circle one):   a. too broad   b. too narrow

New Topic Sentence: _____

The Topic Sentence (II)

As you know, a topic sentence makes a general statement and limits the scope of a paragraph. A good topic sentence also performs these important tasks:

1. **It establishes a contract between the reader and the writer.** The topic sentence leads the reader to expect that the rest of the paragraph will contain certain ideas or information. The writer is obliged to meet the reader's expectations.

2. **It captures the reader's attention.** The topic sentence should be interesting enough to make the reader want to continue reading.

Keeping a Contract with the Reader. The topic sentence of the following paragraph is inappropriate. It leads the reader to expect information that the paragraph does not contain. Write an appropriate topic sentence to replace the one given in the paragraph.

Elephants are among the most intelligent creatures on earth. In a single day, an African elephant eats over 750 pounds of shrubs, leaves, grass, and other plant materials. The Asiatic elephant, which is smaller, eats about 650 pounds of food daily. Because of their enormous appetites, elephants must roam continually from place to place in search of food.

New Topic Sentence: _____

_____

Writing Interesting Topic Sentences. Rewrite the following dull sentences. Make your revised sentences interesting enough to serve as the topic sentences of paragraphs.

DULL TOPIC SENTENCE: Something unusual happened during our camping trip.

INTERESTING TOPIC SENTENCE: We had just made camp when we saw the eerie lights across the lake.

1.   Television commercials are often not well made. _____

_____

_____

2.   I have decided on one career that might be interesting to pursue. _____

_____

_____

3.   I would like to tell you about a person I met one time. _____

_____

_____

4   Collecting stamps is a worthwhile hobby. _____

_____

Using Sensory Details

Once you have properly limited your topic sentence, your next step is to gather details to develop your main idea. Some paragraphs are best developed by using **sensory details**. These are details that tell how your subject *looks*, *sounds*, *tastes*, *feels*, or *smells*.

Using Sensory Details. Imagine that you are standing on a busy street corner. Using sensory details, write three sentences, as follows:

1. Describe something you can see. _____

_____

2. Describe something you can hear. _____

_____

3. Describe something you can smell. _____

_____

Developing a Paragraph with Sensory Details. Choose one of the topics below. Then, write a narrowed topic sentence and a list of sensory details you could use to develop this topic.

> **Possible Topics**
>
> 1. A circus or carnival   3. A music video
> 2. A room in a museum   4. A football game

Narrowed Topic Sentence: _____

_____

Sensory Details

Sight: _____

_____

_____

Sound: _____

_____

_____

Other: _____

_____

Using Facts and Statistics

Another way to develop a paragraph is to use **facts and statistics**. These provide specific data about your topic. Notice how facts and statistics are used to develop the following paragraph.

The desert camel has a remarkable energy system that allows it to do without water for days. It has a type of closed, internal air conditioning system that circulates the same water again and again. This forestalls sweating until body temperature reaches 105 degrees. The camel can refrain from drinking water eight days in summer and fifty-six days in winter. At a rare watering hole, it can consume one hundred quarts of water in the record time of ten minutes. Because of its ability to store and recycle water internally, the camel is often the envy of its thirsty rider.

Developing a Paragraph with Facts and Statistics. Read the following pre-writing notes for a paragraph. These notes include a topic sentence and a list of facts and statistics. Draw a line through each fact or statistic that does not support the topic sentence.

Topic Sentence: The redwoods and sequoias are the largest trees on earth.

Facts and Statistics:

1. Redwoods grow to the height of a thirty-story building.

2. The outer bark of a tree is known as *cork*.

3. The oldest trees on earth are the bristlecone pines.

4. Giant sequoias are shorter than redwoods, but they are much bigger around.

5. The tallest of the redwoods is 368 feet high.

6. The first trees on earth were the seed ferns.

7. Sequoia, a Cherokee Indian, invented a system of writing and taught this system to his people.

8. The largest tree in the world is the General Sherman Tree, a giant sequoia located in Sequoia National Park.

9. Scientists can tell the age of a tree by carefully studying the rings in a cross-section of the trunk.

10. Yew trees are often grown in cemeteries; the wood from them is commonly used to make bows for archery.

11. In ancient times, tree spirits were worshiped in many parts of Europe, the Mideast, Africa, and the Americas.

12. Some redwoods and sequoias are so large that people have actually lived in them.

13. Maples and oaks are among the most common shade trees.

14. Trees supply lumber for construction and pulp for making paper.

15. Several of the giant sequoias are approximately one hundred feet in circumference at the base.

Using Specific Examples

Sometimes the topic sentence will consist of a general idea that is best supported through the use of **specific examples**. Note how the following paragraph uses specific examples to illustrate Thomas Jefferson's architectural imagination.

Thomas Jefferson demonstrated his architectural imagination in his design of Monticello. Locating his mansion on a mountaintop was unique. Constructing it of brick and stone was unusual. Servants' quarters, in separate buildings covered with terraces, were connected to the main house by underground tunnels. The entrance hall contained a clock that told the day as well as the hour. Glass doors opened simultaneously at the touch of a hand because of concealed pulleys. A dining room fireplace contained a small hidden elevator that brought up wine bottles from the cellar. The pantry was connected to the dining room by a swinging door. Overhead, in one of the ceilings, a dialed compass linked to a weather vane on the roof indicated wind direction. These are but a few of the architectural marvels for which Jefferson was responsible.

Developing a Paragraph with Specific Examples. Choose one of the following topics or one of your own. Write a narrowed topic sentence to introduce your main idea. Then, write one or more specific examples that you could use to develop this idea in a finished paragraph.

> **Possible Topics**
> 1. The quickness with which science fiction becomes fact
> 2. The value of a sense of humor
> 3. Things children learn from one another
> 4. Why being in a hospital needn't be depressing

Narrowed Topic Sentence: _____

_____

_____

Specific Example(s):

_____

_____

_____

_____

_____

_____

_____

_____

Using an Incident or Anecdote

An **incident** or **anecdote** is simply a very short story. You can use such a story to illustrate a point made in the topic sentence of a paragraph. Notice how an anecdote is used to illustrate the topic sentence in the paragraph below.

Sometimes the best ideas seem to come out of nowhere. Once, for example, Robert Frost stayed up all night working on a long poem entitled "New Hampshire." The poem was an enormous labor, and by morning Frost was exhausted. He wandered outside onto a busy city sidewalk. Suddenly, the words to "Stopping by Woods on a Snowy Evening" occurred to him as though they had been whispered in his ear. "New Hampshire," the poem he had struggled with for hours, was a failure. However, the little poem that simply came to him effortlessly turned out to be a masterpiece.

Developing a Paragraph by Using an Incident or Anecdote. Choose one of the following topic sentences and underline it. Then, describe an incident or anecdote that you could use to develop this topic sentence.

Topic Sentence:

1. Dreams are often extremely realistic.
2. Caring for a pet can teach you a great deal about yourself.
3. Fear of the unfamiliar is extremely common, especially among children.
4. In any dangerous situation, the most important rule to remember is to remain calm.

Incident or Anecdote: _____

_____

_____

_____

_____

_____

_____

_____

_____

_____

_____

_____

_____

Organizing Ideas in Paragraphs

Once you have gathered information for a paragraph, you must present this information in a logical way. Use any of the following methods of organization:

chronological order   order of importance   comparison
spatial order   order of familiarity   contrast

Organizing Ideas in Paragraphs. Decide which of the methods of organization mentioned above was used in each of the following paragraphs.

1. One of the most colorful folk costumes is that of the Scottish Highlanders. The costume includes boots, or *brogues*; plaid stockings; and a *kilt*, or pleated skirt. In front of the kilt hangs an ornamental pouch. Above the kilt is a *doublet*, or jacket. The Highlander may also wear a plaid cape, or *mantle*, which is attached at the shoulder with a brooch, and a traditional *bonnet*, or cap.

Method of Organization: _____

2. Readers all over the world know Jane Austen as the author of such delightful novels as *Pride and Prejudice* and *Sense and Sensibility*. Less familiar to most readers is the history of English kings and queens that Austen wrote as a child. This seldom read little book shows that, even at an early age, Austen had a marvelous sense of humor and a gift for choosing the right word.

Method of Organization: _____

3. Quilting and needlepoint are very similar. Both involve a few basic patterns or stitches. These patterns and stitches can be combined in numerous ways. Each craft also requires careful and precise hand sewing. The final product in each case—a quilt or a piece of needlework—has an interesting combination of texture and design.

Method of Organization: _____

4. Roberto Walker Clemente was truly one of the greatest baseball players of all time. Born in 1934, in Carolina, Puerto Rico, Clemente made a name for himself as a right fielder for the Pittsburgh Pirates. In 1966, Clemente was voted the National League's most valuable player. By September of 1972, he had become the eleventh player in major league history to get over three thousand hits. In all, Clemente received four National League batting titles during his career, and his lifetime batting average was an impressive .317.

Method of Organization: _____

5. World history textbooks often contain broad references to "Greek and Roman civilization." However, these two sources of Western culture were not at all alike. The Greeks were playwrights, philosophers, and artists. The Romans were soldiers, builders, merchants, politicians, and tradesmen. Thus the two civilizations represented the opposite human tendencies of reflection and action, thinking and doing.

Method of Organization: _____

The Narrative Paragraph

A **narrative paragraph** tells a real or imaginary story. Some narratives are told from the **first-person point of view**, using pronouns such as *I*, *we*, *me*, and *us*. Others are told from the **third-person point of view**, using pronouns such as *he*, *she*, and *they*.

When planning a narrative paragraph, first choose a story to tell. Then, choose a point of view. Finally, list the events of your story in chronological order.

When writing your paragraph, use transitional devices to show the order of events. The following transitional words and phrases are often used in narratives:

once	instantly	finally
suddenly	meanwhile	soon
then	later	for a while

Planning a Narrative Paragraph. Choose one of the following topics or one of your own. Then, make a set of pre-writing notes for a narrative paragraph.

Possible Topics

1. An imaginary incident from the life of a historical character
2. An imaginary incident involving beings from another planet
3. A real incident involving strong emotions
4. A real incident that changed your attitudes, values, or opinions

---

Narrowed Topic: _____

_____

Point of View (first or third person): _____

Events (in chronological order):

1. _____

2. _____

3. _____

4. _____

5. _____

6. _____

7. _____

8. _____

Using these notes, write a draft of your paragraph. Then, revise your draft and make a final copy.

The Descriptive Paragraph

A **descriptive paragraph** presents a picture of a person, place, or thing. When planning a descriptive paragraph, gather sensory details that show how your subject looks, feels, tastes, sounds, and smells. Then, organize your details in spatial order. You may present your details from *side to side*, *top to bottom*, *near to far*, or *far to near*. When writing your paragraph, use transitional words and phrases such as the following to show place or position:

to the right	above	beyond
next to	below	closer
in the middle	at the top	in the background

Writing a Descriptive Paragraph. Choose one of the following topics or one of your own. Then, make pre-writing notes for a descriptive paragraph.

Possible Topics

1. A room in your school
2. Someone you admire
3. A place used for recreation or entertainment
4. An unusual gadget or machine

Narrowed Topic: _____

Sensory Details (in spatial order): _____

_____

_____

_____

_____

_____

_____

_____

_____

Topic Sentence: _____

_____

Order Used (circle one):   side to side   top to bottom   bottom to top
                           near to far   far to near

Using these notes, write a first draft of your paragraph. Then, revise your draft and make a final copy.

The Expository Paragraph (I)

A paragraph written to explain something or to present information is called an **expository paragraph**. One type of expository paragraph is the **paragraph that explains a process**. Such a paragraph may give directions. It may also tell how something works or happens. When writing a paragraph of this kind, present each step in the process in chronological order. Use transitional words and phrases to make the order of the steps clear. Some transitions often used for this purpose are *first*, *next*, and *finally*.

Planning a Paragraph That Explains a Process. Choose one of the following topics or one of your own. Then, make pre-writing notes for a paragraph that explains a process. Write your narrowed topic, your list of steps, and a topic sentence. Arrange your steps in chronological order.

Possible Topics

1. How to pitch a tent
2. How to do some simple household task
3. How to run for a class or club office at your school
4. How some natural process occurs

Narrowed Topic: _____

_____

Steps in the Process (in chronological order):

_____

_____

_____

_____

_____

_____

_____

_____

_____

Topic Sentence: _____

_____

Use your notes to write a draft of your explanatory paragraph. Then, revise the paragraph and make a final copy.

The Expository Paragraph (II)

Another kind of expository paragraph is the **paragraph that defines**. Such paragraphs should be organized as follows:

1. Begin with a topic sentence that places the term to be defined into a general category. This sentence should also describe a specific characteristic of the thing you are defining.

EXAMPLE: An epic is a long narrative poem   about the adventures of a hero.
                    general category   **specific characteristic**

2. Then, write several sentences that present specific characteristics of the thing you are defining. Show how the thing being defined differs from other things of its kind.

Writing the Topic Sentence of a Paragraph That Defines. The following are incomplete topic sentences from paragraphs that define. Rewrite these sentences. Supply the missing parts of each sentence. You may wish to refer to a dictionary or encyclopedia.

1. A pheasant is a bird. _____

_____

2. It is the largest city in the United States. _____

_____

3. Swahili is a language. _____

_____

4. A gondola is long and narrow and has a pointed prow and stern. _____

_____

5. This dangerous phenomenon often accompanies storms and causes fires. _____

_____

6. A turban is a type of headdress. _____

_____

7. Pterodactyls were reptiles. _____

_____

8. Buddhism is ancient and originated in India. _____

_____

9. These are students in the second year of high school or college. _____

_____

10. A cello is an instrument. _____

_____

The Expository Paragraph (III)

A third type of expository paragraph is the **paragraph that gives reasons**. Such a paragraph shows why something is true or why something should be. The paragraph may explain that something is true *because* of certain facts. It may explain that an action or opinion is right *because* certain facts support it. Ideas in a paragraph that gives reasons should be presented in order of importance, using transitional words and phrases such as *one reason* and *most importantly*.

Planning a Paragraph That Gives Reasons. Choose one of the following topics and narrow it. Next, write a topic sentence that states a belief, fact, or opinion. Then, list two reasons that support the statement you made in your topic sentence. Give these reasons in order of importance. Finally, list details you can use to develop each of your reasons.

Possible Topics

1. Why people should read newspapers
2. Why safety rules and regulations are important
3. Why learning basic mathematics is valuable
4. Why people should exercise regularly

Narrowed Topic: _____

Topic Sentence: _____

_____

Reason #1: _____

_____

Supporting Details: _____

_____

_____

_____

Reason #2: _____

_____

Supporting Details: _____

_____

_____

_____

Use your notes to write a draft of your explanatory paragraph. Then, revise the paragraph and make a final copy.

The Persuasive Paragraph

A **persuasive paragraph** is a type of expository paragraph. Its purpose is to persuade readers to accept the logic behind an opinion or to adopt a specific point of view. The following are two of the many ways to organize a persuasive paragraph:

1. Begin with a topic sentence that states an opinion. In the rest of the paragraph, support the opinion with facts, statistics, and other evidence. Present your supporting ideas in order of importance, ending with the strongest and most effective reason.

2. Begin with a topic sentence that presents an issue or question. Then, present possible arguments against your position and show why these arguments are weak. Finally, give the arguments in favor of your position.

Developing a Persuasive Paragraph. Choose one of the following topic sentences. Write a sentence that presents an argument *against* your position on the question expressed in the topic sentence. Then, write a sentence that explains why the argument against your position is weak. Finally, write two sentences that present arguments in favor of your position.

Topic Sentence (underline one):

1. Should public schools be in session all year long?

2. Should businesses be required to provide day-care centers for working mothers?

3. Should news programs include "on the scene" interviews with people in distress?

4. Should the legal driving age be raised?

Argument Against Your Position: _____

_____

_____

Weaknesses of Argument Against Your Position: _____

_____

_____

_____

Arguments for Your Position:

1. _____

_____

2. _____

_____

Use your notes to make a draft of your paragraph. Then, revise the paragraph and make a final copy.

Review: Types of Paragraphs

TYPES OF
PARAGRAPHS 46

Read the following paragraphs. Then, answer the questions that follow.

1. From our fourth-story window, we could see the entire parade. At its head was an enormous helium-filled balloon in the shape of an elephant. Behind the elephant was a high school marching band, complete with musicians, baton-twirlers, and a drill team. Following the marching band were two floats, a team of miniature horses, assorted circus animals, and an Uncle Sam character on stilts. Then, escorted by police cars and motorcycles, came the candidate's limousine.

a. Is this paragraph narrative, descriptive, or expository? _____

b. What is the topic sentence of this paragraph? _____

_____

c. Is this paragraph organized in chronological order, in spatial order, or in order of

importance? _____

d. Write two transitional words or phrases used in this paragraph. _____

_____

2. Tracing a family tree is not terribly difficult. Begin by simply talking with the oldest members of your family or with long-time family friends. Ask them for the names and birthplaces of as many family members as they can remember. Next, request to see old photographs, scrapbooks, and other relevant documents that your friends and relatives have. As you receive information concerning family members, write everything down on note cards. Make sure not to confuse names, dates, and places. After you have learned all you can from friends and relatives, check records of births, deaths, marriages, and property ownership in government offices of the cities and counties in which your family members have lived. In addition, check the churches, temples, or synagogues that family members have attended for any significant documents they might possess. Doing all of this will take some time, but you will be rewarded by being able to put together a story that is like no other—the story of your family.

a. Is this paragraph narrative, descriptive, or expository? _____

b. What is the topic sentence of this paragraph? _____

_____

c. Is this paragraph organized in chronological order, in spatial order, or in order of

importance? _____

d. Write two transitional words or phrases used in this paragraph. _____

_____

Copyright © 1985 by McDougal, Littell & Company

Choosing a Subject

A **composition** is a group of paragraphs dealing with a single topic or idea. Usually, one paragraph, called the **introduction**, states the main idea of the composition. The paragraphs of the **body** develop this main idea completely. A final paragraph, the **conclusion**, ties together the ideas presented in the introduction and body.

The first step in writing a composition is to choose a **subject**. Good subjects may be drawn from imagination or experience. The subject you choose should be one that interests you, that is familiar to you, and that has value for you. The following are all good sources of ideas for compositions:

Personal observation   Brainstorming   Interviews
Journal entries   Clustering   Discussions

Exploring Ideas for Compositions. Answer the following questions in complete sentences. Then, based on your answers, write three possible composition topics.

1. Describe an important turning point in your life. _____

_____

2. Describe an important learning experience you have had. _____

_____

3. Name someone who has had an important influence on the development of your

values, beliefs, or personality. _____

_____

4. Describe a change that you would like to see take place in the world around you.

_____

5. Name something that creates in you feelings of wonder or curiosity. _____

_____

6. Name some activity that you like or dislike intensely and tell how you feel about it.

_____

7. Name someone whom you admire and tell why. _____

_____

8. Name another time or place you would like to visit and tell why. _____

_____

Topic 1: _____

Topic 2: _____

Topic 3: _____

Planning a Composition

Choosing a subject is only the first step in planning a composition. After you choose a subject, you must narrow it so that it can be completely developed in a few paragraphs.

Next, you must identify your purpose and audience. Your **purpose** may be *to tell a story*, *to explain* something, or *to describe* a person, place, or thing. Your **audience** is all the people who will read your composition. The audience will determine the amount of information you include, the words you choose, and the explanations you give.

Once you have identified your purpose and audience, you must then gather information about your narrowed topic. Decide upon the kind of information you will include: specific examples, reasons, facts, statistics, or sensory details. This informaton may come from your own experience or from interviews and discussions. It may also come from books, magazines, newspapers, or reference works. Make certain that the information you gather is appropriate to your topic, purpose, and audience.

Identifying Your Topic, Purpose, and Audience. Imagine that you are going to write two compositions dealing with high school extracurricular activities.

One composition will be read to a group of parents, teachers, and administrators. These are the people who will decide how funds for extracurricular activities at your school will be spent in the future.

The other composition will be read to a group of incoming freshmen. These freshmen are interested in learning more about specific extracurricular activities that are open to them.

For each of these audiences, write a narrowed topic that is suitable for a five-paragraph composition. Then, write a sentence explaining the purpose of each composition. Be specific, and be prepared to explain why your statements of topic and purpose differ.

Composition 1

Narrowed Topic: _____

_____

Purpose: _____

_____

_____

Audience: A group of parents, teachers, and administrators

Composition 2

Narrowed Topic: _____

_____

Purpose: _____

_____

_____

Audience: A group of incoming freshmen

Organizing a Composition

After you gather details for a composition, you must then put these details into a logical order. Begin by sorting your details into groups of related ideas. Then, put your groups of ideas into a logical order. Finally, organize the ideas within each group. Use any of the following methods of organization between and within paragraphs:

chronological order   order of importance
spatial order   comparison and contrast

Turn each group of ideas into a separate paragraph of your rough draft.

Organizing Ideas in a Composition. Follow the directions given below.

1. Imagine that you are going to write a composition on the influences that affect clothing styles among teenagers. List four major influences and then number them from **1** to **4**, in order of importance.

_____   _____

_____   _____

_____   _____

_____   _____

2. Imagine that you want to write a composition describing three paintings that you have seen in an exhibit. One of the paragraphs describes a landscape, the details of which are given below. Number these details **1** through **4**, in spatial order from near to far.

_____   Trees, in their autumn colors, on the opposite shore

_____   In the background, a brilliant blue sky

_____   Snow-capped mountains rising up from behind the trees

_____   In the foreground, a lake and a fishing boat

3. Imagine that you are going to write a composition for an audience of students who are about to enter high school. The purpose of the composition will be to explain what high school is like. In the first paragraph of your composition, you plan to compare and contrast high school and junior high or middle school. List two similarities, or points of comparison, that you could use to begin the paragraph. Then, list two differences, or points of contrast, that you could use to conclude the paragraph.

Similarities: a. _____

          b. _____

Differences: c. _____

          d. _____

The Introductory Paragraph

The **introductory paragraph** of a composition serves two important functions. It catches the reader's attention. It also tells the reader what the rest of the composition will be about. There are many types of introductory paragraphs. The following are some of the most effective:

1. **The Paragraph That Makes a Direct Appeal.** In a paragraph of this kind, speak directly to the reader. Tie your topic directly to the reader's own experiences or feelings.

2. **The Paragraph That Uses a Personal Approach.** Begin by describing a personal experience that relates to your topic. Make your attitude toward the topic apparent to the reader.

3. **The Paragraph That Describes an Overall Effect.** Describe your subject using sensory details that create a particular mood.

4. **The Paragraph That Arouses Curiosity.** Invite the reader to find the answer to a question by reading the rest of the composition.

Recognizing Types of Introductions. Read the following introductory paragraphs. Tell what type of introduction each paragraph is by writing **1**, **2**, **3**, or **4** in the space provided. Then, tell what topic each paragraph is introducing.

1. Classical mythology is full of wondrous creatures. The centaur is half horse and half man, the furies are half women and half birds, and the griffin is half eagle and half lion. As strange as these fanciful beings seem, there is one real creature that is even stranger: the euglena. This tiny organism is both a plant and an animal. How, you might ask, is this possible?

Type of Introduction: _____   Topic: _____

2. High school students often feel that more work is required of them than they can possibly get done. Almost every student has had this experience, and you can expect the feeling to occur more and more frequently as you grow older. Therefore, now is a good time to think about how to organize your time most effectively. One excellent way to do this is to begin making a weekly activities schedule.

Type of Introduction: _____   Topic: _____

Writing an Introduction. Imagine that you are going to write a composition on the proper care and feeding of some animal. On a separate piece of paper, write a rough draft of an introduction for this composition. Then revise your draft and copy it onto the lines below.

_____

_____

_____

_____

_____

The Body

The paragraphs of the **body** of a composition should develop and support the ideas presented in the introduction. Each paragraph of the body should consist of a topic sentence and several sentences that relate to the topic sentence.

To give the body a feeling of unity and coherence, use transitional devices to tie your ideas together. A **transitional device** is a word or phrase that shows how an idea is related to the ideas that come before and after it. The following transitional devices are often used in compositions:

1. A word or phrase that indicates time: *first, before, meanwhile, finally, eventually, afterwards, today, in the meantime, next, after*

2. A word that shows the relationships between ideas: *also, because, therefore, moreover, too, and, besides, similarly*

3. A word that shows an opposite point of view: *but, while, on the other hand, nevertheless, however, although, in contrast, yet*

4. A word that repeats a word used earlier: Cats are known for their *independence*. *Independence* is a quality to be respected.

5. A synonym of a word used earlier: The students in the class developed a strong sense of *camaraderie*. This feeling of *fellowship* made it possible for us to have many interesting discussions.

6. A pronoun that refers to a word used earlier: *Wayne* wants to work as a recording engineer. *He* has already had experience mixing sound for several local bands.

Using Transitional Devices. In the exercises below, you are given one sentence and a transitional word or phrase to introduce a second sentence. Complete the second sentence in each pair.

1. The immigrants now understood what freedom meant. *Their* _____

_____

2. Rita liked living in the city. *On the other hand*, _____

_____

3. Spiro shopped for pita bread and tomatoes. *In the meantime*, _____

_____

4. Knowing basic carpentry gives one a feeling of accomplishment. *Moreover*, _____

_____

5. Anna has a special talent for amusing young children. *She* _____

_____

6. All his life, Hector had wanted to learn about psychology. *Psychology* _____

_____

The Conclusion

The **conclusion** ties together the ideas presented in the rest of the composition. It also indicates to the reader that the composition is finished. The following are two methods you can use to conclude a composition:

1. Repeat, using different words, the ideas presented in the introductory paragraph.
2. Summarize or comment on the ideas in the rest of the composition.

Writing a Conclusion. Read the following introduction and body of a composition. Then, write an appropriate conclusion.

Learning To Draw

The ability to draw is usually considered a special talent—something that only a gifted few are capable of doing well. However, almost everyone learns to write the letters of the alphabet. When a person makes such a letter, he or she is actually *drawing* it. Since almost anyone can learn to write letters, it follows that almost anyone can learn to draw reasonably well. To learn to draw, you must simply study drawing as carefully as you once studied handwriting.

The first thing you must do to learn to draw is to practice regularly. Carry a sketchbook with you at all times, and draw whenever you get a chance. Do not worry about subject matter, and do not be discouraged if your first efforts are crude. With practice, your drawing will doubtless improve.

Another action you can take to improve your drawing is to find a teacher. Ask someone who draws well to show you some of his or her techniques. If you do not have any friends who are artists, find a good book on drawing such as *Drawing on the Right Side of the Brain*. Such an instruction manual will teach you many simple techniques that will enable you to produce drawings of surprising quality.

Finally, once you start drawing, don't stop. Remember that it took a while for you to learn how to make the funny squiggles and lines of the alphabet. Expect to spend an equal amount of time learning how to make representations of people and things.

_____

_____

_____

_____

_____

_____

_____

_____

_____

_____

_____

_____

Revising a Composition

The final stage in writing a composition is revision. As you revise, try to improve the unity and coherence of your rough draft. Also, try to replace dull or vague language with language that is vivid and precise. Once your revision is complete, proofread your composition for errors in grammar, usage, and mechanics. Correct any errors you find.

Revising a Composition. Study the revisions made in the following introduction to a composition. Then, answer the questions below.

Camping *the Old-Fashioned Way*

Modern Campers are peculiar creatures. Gone are the days of roughing it with a back pack and a two-person pup tent. *However,* There are some poeple who *still* prefer the old way *of camping.* If you are *you know that there are but a few supplies that a camper really needs.* one of these poeple, there are some things you need to know. A camper of today must get back to nature in style. He or she must have a *recreational vehicle* van that is like a house with wheels and an engine. Other *essential* equipment includes a portable, battery operated television; An AM/ FM radio/casette player, And a beeper to keep the camper *in constant contact with his* worried about stuff in the *or her office.* outside world. For the camper who is interested in fishing, *there* their is a gadget that uses *even* *sonar* *locate fish* waves and stuff to find objects in the water beneath a boat. *In short,* The modern camper has so many conveniences that a week in the woods might well seem just like *a week at home or* any old ordinary *at work.* week. Camping is also good exercise.

1. Has the title been improved? If so, how? _____

_____

2. Why were the third and fourth sentences moved to the end of the paragraph?

_____

3. In what ways did the writer make the language of the paragraph more precise?

_____

_____

4. Has this paragraph been proofread? How can you tell? _____

_____

5. Why was the last sentence deleted? _____

_____

A **narrative composition** is one that tells a story. A **simple narrative** is a composition that presents a series of events leading to a conclusion. A **complex narrative**, or short story, is a composition that tells about the development and resolution of a conflict. Every narrative contains the following elements:

1. **Plot.** This is the series of events in the narrative.
2. **Characters.** These are the people or animals in the narrative.
3. **Setting.** This is the place and time of the narrative.
4. **Point of View.** This is the angle from which the narrative is told. A narrative may be told from the first-person point of view, using pronouns such as *I* and *we*. It may also be told from the third-person point of view, using pronouns such as *he*, *she*, and *they*.

Planning a Simple Narrative. Think of a story from your own life. The story should be one that took place in a single setting and that involved no more than two or three major characters. On the lines below, make pre-writing notes for this story. First, give the names and ages of your characters and a general description of each. Then, describe your setting using vivid sensory details. Finally, list the events of the story in chronological order.

Characters: _____

_____

_____

_____

_____

Setting: _____

_____

_____

_____

_____

Events (in chronological order):

_____

_____

_____

_____

_____

_____

_____

The Narrative Composition (II)

In addition to plot, character, setting, and point of view, most complex narratives, or short stories, contain the following elements:

1. **Conflict.** This is the struggle or problem faced by the main character or characters. A narrative can show an individual in conflict with society, with himself or herself, against a supernatural force, or against nature.

2. **Theme.** This is the central idea of the narrative. The theme may be an impression or idea that the writer wants to convey. It may also be a moral or philosophical message.

Developing a Conflict and Theme. Read the following opening to a short story. Then, answer the questions below.

Sharon Anderson was one of the finest pilots who ever climbed into a plane. Both as an astronaut and test pilot, she had had a distinguished career, logging over eight thousand hours in flight. Of course, she knew how to handle all the standard emergencies, such as engine trouble, terrible weather, and other planes in her flight path. However, she didn't know quite how to handle what she now saw through her cockpit window, sitting atop a cloud at twenty thousand feet.

1. What is the setting of this story? _____

_____

2. What information does the opening provide about the major character? _____

_____

3. If you were writing this story, what conflict might you introduce? _____

_____

_____

4. Given the conflict you have chosen, what theme could your story have? _____

_____

_____

Planning a Complex Narrative. Choose one of the following topics or one of your own. On a separate piece of paper, make pre-writing notes for a complex narrative. Include in your notes descriptions of your characters, setting, and conflict. Then, list the events in your story. Finally, describe your theme and tell whether you plan to write from the first-person or third-person point of view.

Possible topics: An incident involving a visitor from another place
An incident involving a natural disaster
An incident involving a great achievement
An incident involving a famous person
An incident involving a family celebration

The Descriptive Composition (I)

A **descriptive composition** uses words to create a picture of a person, place, or thing. Follow these guidelines when writing a descriptive composition:

1. Use sensory details to make your subject come alive. Describe how your subject *looks*, *sounds*, *feels*, *tastes*, and *smells*.
2. Choose details that will create a particular mood, or feeling, in the mind of your reader.

Choosing Appropriate Sensory Details. Imagine that you are writing a descriptive composition about a beach. The following is a list of the details from your pre-writing notes. Draw a line through each detail that could *not* be used to create a mood of fun and relaxation.

1. People on surfboards
2. The biting of sand flies and midges
3. Brightly colored beach towels and bathing suits
4. Storm clouds
5. Sharp objects embedded in the sand
6. A volleyball game on the shore
7. Sunburns
8. Sand castles
9. A vendor selling frozen yogurt
10. Cold water lashing against boulders along the shoreline
11. Children gathering seashells
12. Eye strain caused by the glare of the sun

Using Sensory Details To Establish Mood. Imagine that you are going to write a descriptive composition about an amusement park. Choose a mood that you would like to create in your composition. Then, list sensory details that will help you to create this mood.

Subject: An amusement park   Mood: _____

Sensory Details: _____

_____

_____

_____

_____

_____

_____

_____

_____

_____

_____

When writing a description, try to give your reader the feeling of being in an actual place. To do this, present your subject from a particular physical point of view. The **physical point of view** is the place or location from which the writer and reader observe the subject. Describe only those things that can be seen, heard, felt, tasted, and smelled from the point of view you have chosen.

Choosing a Physical Point of View. The following paragraph from a descriptive composition has been written from the point of view of a home plate umpire during a baseball game. Rewrite this description from the point of view of someone sitting in the stands high above the playing field.

> To me, the best part of a baseball game is the anxious moment just before the first ball is pitched. As a home plate umpire, I see this moment from a unique perspective. In front of me, the catcher crouches in readiness. In front of the catcher, the batter looms large and powerful as he poises himself for action. The players on the opposite team appear, in contrast, small and insignificant. They are lost in the sea of green that makes up the diamond. Beyond them, of course, is the crowd, which seems not like a group of individuals but like a single enormous, vital creature, watching us expectantly, like a cat.

_____

_____

_____

_____

_____

_____

_____

_____

_____

_____

_____

_____

_____

_____

_____

A **composition that explains a process** tells how to do something or how something works. When writing such a composition, use a direct, straightforward style. In the introduction, state the process you are going to explain and try to interest your readers in this process. In the body, write separate paragraphs to describe each major step in the process. In the conclusion, present the last step in the process, describe the finished product, or explain why the process is valuable or important.

Writing a Composition That Explains a Process. The following paragraphs are from the body of a composition that explains a process. On the lines below, write a conclusion for this composition.

Making a Book

Before the modern age of mechanized typesetting and printing, most books were made by hand. The processes used were quite simple, and the products—the books themselves—were often extremely beautiful. By copying some of the techniques used in the past, you can easily create a book for your own writing. All you need to do is to follow a few simple instructions.

To make a book, you will need the following materials: twenty-four sheets of 8½″ × 14″ white typing paper, sewing thread, a sewing needle, and scissors. You will also need gauze, glue, two pieces of 8½″ × 7½″ cardboard, and one piece of 18½″ × 11½″ fabric. These materials can be obtained at local fabric shops, office supply shops, and department stores.

Begin by putting together the pages of your book. Lay three sheets of typing paper on top of one another. Fold the paper down the middle to form a little booklet that is 8½″ deep and 7″ wide. Repeat this procedure with all your paper. Then, bind your booklets together. First, sew together the pages of each booklet using your needle and thread. Stitch along the crease, or fold, in each booklet. Second, lay your booklets on top of one another, with the folds to your left. Cut three strips of gauze to the size of the left, or folded, edge of your stack of booklets. Dip your gauze in watered-down glue and apply each strip to the left edge of the stack.

Next, make your cover and attach your stack of booklets to it. Start by laying your piece of fabric on a table. Place your pieces of cardboard on top of the fabric, leaving a ½″ space between the two pieces of cardboard and 1½″ between the pieces of cardboard and the edges of the fabric. Fold the edges of the fabric over the cardboard and glue them down. Then, place your stack of bound booklets, folded side down, on top of the space between the two pieces of cardboard. Glue the first page of your stack of booklets to the inside front cover and the last page to the inside back cover. Close your book and let the glue dry.

_____

_____

_____

_____

_____

_____

The **expository composition that defines** is used to introduce the reader to an unfamiliar term, object, or idea. Begin by placing the term to be defined into a general category. Then, identify several distinguishing characteristics of the term. Develop your topic using sensory details, facts, statistics, or examples. Organize your ideas from general to specific or from most familiar to least familiar.

Gathering Information for a Composition That Defines. Study the pairs of words given below. First, write the general category that both words belong to. Then, list details that distinguish the words from one another. Use a dictionary or encyclopedia as necessary.

1. *Harpsichord . . . . piano*   General category: _____

   a. Specific characteristics of *harpsichord*: _____

   _____

   b. Specific characteristics of *piano*: _____

   _____

2. *galleon . . . . gondola*   General category: _____

   a. Specific characteristics of *galleon*: _____

   _____

   b. Specific characteristics of *gondola*: _____

   _____

3. *calculator . . . . abacus*   General category: _____

   a. Specific characteristics of *calculator*: _____

   _____

   b. Specific characteristics of *abacus*: _____

   _____

4. *dictionary . . . . thesaurus*   General category: _____

   a. Specific characteristics of *dictionary*: _____

   _____

   b. Specific characteristics of *thesaurus*: _____

   _____

The **composition that gives reasons** is another type of expository composition. It presents reasons why a particular fact or opinion is true or should be true. In the introductory paragraph, you state the idea or opinion that will control the content of the composition. In the body, you present reasons: facts, statistics, examples, incidents, or anecdotes that support your main idea. In each paragraph of the body, present one major reason and details that support or develop this reason. You may use any of the following methods of organization: *least important to most important*, *most familiar to least familiar*, or *comparison and contrast.* The kind of organization you use will depend on the types of reasons you gather and on the strength of those reasons.

Choosing Supporting Ideas for a Composition That Gives Reasons. Write three possible endings for each of the following sentences. Each ending should present a reason that supports the statement made in the first part of the sentence.

1. Music videos are popular because . . .

    a. _____

    b. _____

    c. _____

2. Advertisements cannot always be trusted because . . .

    a. _____

    b. _____

    c. _____

3. People should read regularly because . . .

    a. _____

    b. _____

    c. _____

4. Learning a foreign language is important because . . .

    a. _____

    b. _____

    c. _____

5. Getting some form of exercise every day is important because . . .

    a. _____

    b. _____

    c. _____

Choose one of the topics above or one of your own. Make notes for a composition that gives reasons. Write a rough draft. Then, revise your draft and make a final copy.

The Persuasive Composition

A **persuasive composition** is a type of expository composition. Its purpose is to convince a reader to adopt a specific opinion. The first paragraph of a persuasive composition captures the reader's attention by asking a question, telling a story, or relating an interesting fact. It also states the writer's opinion or belief. Each paragraph of the body presents one major reason or argument to support the statement made in the introductory paragraph.

Planning a Persuasive Composition. Choose one of the following topics or one of your own. Narrow your topic. Then, make pre-writing notes for a persuasive composition.

Possible Topics

1. Why students should join some club or team at your school
2. Why people should take some position on an issue in the news

---

Introduction

Narrowed Topic (an opinion or belief): _____

_____

Details To Capture Reader's Attention: _____

_____

Body

Supporting Argument (first body paragraph): _____

_____

Specific Details: _____

_____

Supporting Argument (second body paragraph): _____

_____

Specific Details: _____

_____

Supporting Argument (third body paragraph): _____

_____

Specific Details: _____

_____

Use your pre-writing notes to write a draft of your persuasive composition. Revise and proofread your draft. Then, make a final copy.

Compositions About Literature

The **composition about literature** differs from other types of composition in that it requires you to use your skills of interpretation and analysis. You must read the poem or story you plan to write about carefully, taking notes on its most important elements.

    1. **Elements of Fiction:** Setting, Mood, Point of View, Theme, Characters (description, importance, motivations), Conflict, Turning Point/Climax

    2. **Elements of Poetry:** Purpose, Theme, Form (free verse, couplet, stanzas), Sound Devices (rhyme, alliteration, assonance, consonance), Imagery (metaphor, simile, personification)

Next, you must choose a topic by deciding which elements interest you the most. List the points you wish to make about the topic. Then, gather support for your ideas by selecting appropriate details, lines, or passages from the story or poem. Finally, you must group your ideas logically, write a rough draft, and make any necessary revisions.

Planning a Composition About Literature. Read the following poem by Adrienne Rich. Then, answer the questions below.

Bears

Wonderful bears that walked my room all night,
Where have you gone, your sleek and fairy fur,
Your eyes' veiled and imperious light?

Brown bears as rich as mocha or as musk,
5 White opalescent bears whose fur stood out
Electric in the deepening dusk,

And great black bears that seemed more blue
    than black,
More violet than blue against the dark—
Where are you now? Upon what track

10 Mutter your muffled paws that used to tread
So softly, surely, up the creakless stair
While I lay listening in bed?

When did I lose you? Whose have you become?
Why do I wait and wait and never hear
15 Your thick nocturnal pacing in my room?
My bears, who keeps you now, in pride and fear?

1.   To whom is the poem addressed? _____

2.   What words are used to describe the bears in the poem? _____

_____

3.   At what time of day did the speaker once see and hear these bears? _____

4.   Were the bears real? How do you know? _____

_____

5.   What is the speaker's attitude toward the bears? _____

6.   What quality of the speaker might these bears symbolize? _____

7.   What has the speaker lost? _____

8.   What is the theme of this poem? _____

_____

Use your notes to write a composition about the theme of this poem. Revise and proofread your rough draft. Then, make a final copy.

Choosing a Subject

A **report** is a piece of writing based on material from sources outside your personal knowledge and experience. Always choose a report topic that interests you. Also choose one that you feel you can make interesting to a reader.

Once you have chosen your topic, narrow it as necessary. An encyclopedia article or the table of contents of a book on your subject may suggest ways to narrow your topic. As you narrow your topic, bear in mind the amount of information available on the topic and the length you want your finished report to be.

Choosing a Subject for a Report. Read the following topics. Circle the number of each topic that is appropriate for a report. A topic is appropriate if it concerns facts from outside sources.

1. How the Early American Pioneers Built Log Cabins

2. Spring—My Favorite Time of Year

3. My Experiences as a Diver

4. How Cameras Work

5. The Early Life of Gwendolyn Brooks

6. The River Nile

7. My First Clarinet Recital

8. Voyager II's Flight to Jupiter

9. The Year I Batted .400

10. What Is a Ballad?

Narrowing a Report Subject. For each of the following broad topics, write a narrowed topic that is appropriate for a five-to-ten-paragraph paper. You may wish to consult a book or encyclopedia.

1. China _____

2. Insects _____

3. Medical Technology _____

4. Famous Musicians _____

5. Disasters _____

6. Games _____

7. The Future _____

8. Astronomy _____

9. Pollution _____

10. Television _____

Preparing To Do Research

After you have chosen and narrowed your topic, the next step is to plan your research. Taking the time to plan your research beforehand will save you time and effort later on.

Begin by identifying your **purpose**. Doing this will help you decide upon what information you will need to gather. Your purpose may be *to inform* your audience about your subject, *to compare and contrast* two subjects, or *to analyze* one subject.

Next, identify your **audience**. This will help you to decide what background information to include in your report. It will also tell you how technical you can be in your explanations and terminology, or word choice.

Finally, make a list of questions that you will need to answer in order to develop your narrowed topic. When conducting your research, look for answers to these questions. Making such a list will help you clarify what you are looking for and will keep you from wasting time gathering irrelevant information.

Preparing for Research. Choose one of the following broad topics for a report. Then, complete the worksheet below.

Possible Topics

1. Desert Life
2. Hurricanes
3. The Middle Ages
4. Sports
5. The Arts
6. The Media

Narrowed Topic: _____

Purpose (circle one):   a. to inform   b. to compare and   c. to analyze
                                                                contrast

Audience (circle one):   a. very familiar   b. somewhat familiar   c. not familiar
                                with topic   with topic   with topic

Questions To Guide Research (list eight):

1. _____
2. _____
3. _____
4. _____
5. _____
6. _____
7. _____
8. _____
9. _____
10. _____

Making a Working Bibliography

Once you have a list of questions to guide your research, you are ready to go to the library to look for sources. Check the card catalog and the *Readers' Guide to Periodical Literature*. When you locate a source, record information about the source on a 3″ × 5″ card. For books, follow this model:

AUTHOR

CALL NUMBER

793.7
B

Borgmann, Dmitri A.

Beyond Language: Adventures in Word and Thought
New York: Charles Scribner's Sons, 1967.

① IDENTIFICATION
NUMBER
TITLE OF BOOK

PUBLISHING
INFORMATION

For magazines and encyclopedias, follow these guidelines:

1. **Magazines.** Give the author, last name first (unless unsigned); the title of the article; the name of the magazine; the date of the magazine; and the page numbers of the article.

2. **Encyclopedias.** Give the title of the article, the name of the book or set, and the year of the edition.

Writing Bibliography Cards. Write bibliography cards for each of the following sources:

1. Book: *Saving the Animals: The World Wildlife Fund Book on Conservation*, call number 333.95 STO, by Bernard Stonehouse. Published in New York by Macmillan in 1981.

2. Magazine Article: "The Roadrunner—Clown of the Desert," by Martha A. Whitson, in *National Geographic*, May 1983, pages 694–702.

Taking Notes

As you read your sources, take notes on the information that you feel is significant to your topic, audience, and purpose. Follow these guidelines:

1. Use 3″ × 5″ cards. Put only one idea on each card.
2. Record the page number of the source of information on each card.
3. Record the number of the bibliography card that identifies the source of your information.
4. Record facts, not opinions. Facts are statements that can be proved true. Opinions are personal views. They cannot be proved true or false.

When writing your note cards, you may reword information from your source or quote your source directly. When rewording, rewrite the information from the source in your own words. When quoting, copy the information onto the note card and place quotation marks around it. Make sure that the quotation is copied word for word. Most of the ideas in a report should be reworded information. Use a quotation only when the author of your source has said something particularly well.

Writing Note Cards. Imagine that you are doing a report on living conditions among nobles in the Middle Ages. Using information from the following selection, make two note cards. The first card should contain reworded information. The second should contain a direct quotation.

> The noble, like the peasant, ate with his fingers, frequently slept on straw, shivered with cold or stifled in smoke-filled rooms in winter, tramped through the mud, and bathed in lakes and rivers. Like the peasant he studied the sky, because he too depended on the fields for his livelihood, and hunted himself the venison he ate. For lack of spacious halls and splendid palaces, even the greatest lords entertained their guests in "flowery meadows" and voluntarily camped out in the open air, taking with them wherever they went what little they possessed in the way of carpets, plates, chests of clothes, and caskets of jewels. They were not above sitting on the grass and weaving themselves crowns of field flowers, or decorating their tents, banqueting halls, and lists with garlands of foliage.
> —ZOE OLDENBOURG

Reworded Information

Direct Quotation

Organizing Information

After you have gathered information for your report, you must organize this information logically. Begin by looking for relationships among the ideas you have gathered. Divide your note cards into groups of related ideas. Then, decide upon the order in which you wish to present each of these idea groups. Finally, decide upon a logical order for the ideas within each group. The information in reports is usually organized in order of importance or in order of familiarity. However, it is also possible to organize some or all of your ideas in chronological order or in spatial order. Another possibility is to develop your subject through comparisons and contrasts.

Organizing Ideas in a Report. Imagine that you are doing a report on the proper care and feeding of pet rabbits. You study your notes and find that they divide into three groups:

A. Handling a Rabbit   B. Housing a Rabbit   C. Feeding a Rabbit

Tell which of these groups the following notes belong to by writing A, B, or C in the blank.

1. A rabbit should never be lifted by its ears or by its legs. _____

2. Another name for a rabbit cage is a "hutch." _____

3. Make sure that the water you leave for the rabbit is fresh. _____

4. Rabbits are not particularly fond of being held. _____

5. The hutch should be warm and dry. _____

6. Supplement the rabbit's diet with carrots, clover, grass, and the like. _____

7. A rabbit's diet includes grains such as barley, wheat, and oats. _____

8. Pick the rabbit up by grabbing the loose skin behind the neck. Make sure to place your other hand under the rabbit for support. _____

9. Place the hutch outside, in a shady area. _____

10. Be careful not to overfeed your rabbit. _____

11. You can also feed the rabbit small amounts of hay. _____

12. Provide a hay-filled box for the rabbit to sleep in. _____

13. Keep the hutch several feet off the ground. _____

14. Be careful when holding the rabbit, for a rabbit's legs are strong, and it is possible that you might be kicked. _____

15. Rabbits do not eat meat; they are vegetarians. _____

16. Dogs have been known to attack pet rabbits; be sure the hutch is strong and securely fastened. _____

Preparing a Final Bibliography

A **final bibliography** is a list of sources that you have used in preparing your report. This list comes at the end of your paper. To write a final bibliography, look over your bibliography cards. Discard cards for sources you did not use. Alphabetize the remaining cards by the author's last name, or by the title of the source if no author is given. Copy all the information from your bibliography cards onto a piece of paper. Follow the format shown below. The first entry is for a magazine, the second is for a book, and the third is for an encyclopedia article.

Bibliography

Hodgson, Bryan. "Wales: The Lyric Land." *National Geographic*, July 1983, pp. 37–63.
Southall, John E. *Wales and Her Language*. Longwood Press, 1977.
"Wales." *World Book Encyclopedia*. 1984 ed.

Writing a Final Bibliography. Imagine that you have written a report about women in modern-day Japan. The following is a list of sources that you have used in your paper:

1. A book called *Japan Today*, written by Clara Desiles, and published in 1981 by Hippocrene Books of New York.

2. An article from the August 1, 1983, edition of *Time* magazine called "Women: a Separate Sphere." The article appears on pages 68–69 and was written by Jane O'Reilly.

3. An article called "Japan" from the 1984 edition of the *World Book Encyclopedia*.

Use this information to write a bibliography for your report.

Facts and Opinions

A **fact** is something that has actually happened or that is really true. Facts can be proved by personal observation or by consulting a reliable source such as a dictionary, encyclopedia, or almanac.

Unlike facts, **opinions** cannot be proved with absolute certainty. However, opinions can be supported by facts. Three main types of opinions are judgments, predictions, and statements of obligation.

Judgments are opinions about the value of things. Such statements often contain words such as *good*, *bad*, *pretty*, *unattractive*, *valuable*, and *worthless*.

Predictions are statements about the future. Such statements tell what someone thinks is going to happen.

Statements of obligation are opinions that tell not how things are but how someone feels things should be. The key words in statements of obligation are *should*, *ought to*, *must*, and similar terms.

Recognizing Facts and Opinions. Tell whether the following statements are facts or opinions. If a statement is an opinion, tell whether it is a judgment, a prediction, or a statement of obligation.

1. Augustino's is an Italian restaurant. _____

2. Augustino's is the best Italian restaurant in town. _____

3. Every American should exercise the right to vote. _____

4. The United States has a democratic form of government. _____

5. Medical researchers will soon find a cure for cancer. _____

6. The American Cancer Society provides funds for cancer research. _____

7. Bird's-nest soup is considered a delicacy in China. _____

8. Bird's-nest soup is delicious. _____

9. A manned space flight to Mars will take place before 1990. _____

10. As yet, no human being has set foot on Mars. _____

11. Videos are very popular among young people today. _____

12. People should not waste time watching videos. _____

13. Picasso was a wonderfully gifted painter. _____

14. Picasso was still painting at the age of ninety. _____

15. The trillium is an exquisite spring wildflower. _____

16. Some trilliums have deep red petals. _____

17. Lowering the speed limit has reduced the number of accidents. _____

18. All drivers should observe the speed limit. _____

Generalization

A **generalization** is a broad statement based on particular facts. Suppose you notice, for instance, that apples, pears, and oranges all grow on trees. You might make the following generalization: "Fruit grows on trees." Later you might notice that grapes grow on vines and that blackberries grow on bushes. These facts show your generalization to be false. Generalizations are only as good as the facts that support them.

An **overgeneralization** is a generalization based on insufficient facts. Often overgeneralizations express opinions. When overgeneralizations name whole groups of people or make absolute statements, they can be irresponsible or harmful. The overgeneralization "All good professional chefs are men" is both untrue and unfair to women chefs.

One way to avoid making overgeneralizations is to be careful about using words that name whole groups. Another is to avoid "absolute words," such as *all*, *every*, *each*, *nobody*, *none*, or *never*. Instead of absolute words, use **qualifiers**, words that limit the range of the statement you are making. Here are some commonly used qualifiers:

TIME WORDS: *usually, often, frequently, sometimes, seldom, rarely*
AMOUNT WORDS: *most, many, much, some, a few, almost no*
DEGREE WORDS: *generally, for the most part, to some extent, somewhat, hardly*

Using Qualifiers To Limit Generalizations. Rewrite the following sentences, using qualifiers from the list above to limit the scope of each generalization.

1. Everyone in California has a beautiful tan. _____

_____

2. There's never anything good to watch on television. _____

_____

3. The best hockey players come from Canada. _____

_____

4. By the end of the century, all shopping will be done with the aid of computers. _____

_____

5. None of the movies being made today are as good as *Gone with the Wind*. _____

_____

6. Teenagers love new wave music. _____

_____

7. No one really prefers baseball to football. _____

_____

8. All cats are terribly independent. _____

_____

Fallacies in Reasoning

Fallacies are errors in reasoning that produce weak arguments. If you learn to recognize common fallacies, you can avoid them in your writing and be alert to them in what you read and hear. The following fallacies are among the most common:

SINGLE CAUSE FALLACY:	describing an event that has several causes as having only one cause
POST HOC, ERGO PROPTER HOC:	assuming that one event was caused by another simply because the events were close to each other in time
EITHER/OR FALLACY:	giving the impression that there are only two alternatives or groups when there are actually more
CIRCULAR REASONING:	trying to prove a statement simply by repeating it in other words
EQUIVOCATION:	taking unfair advantage of the multiple meanings of words

Recognizing Fallacies in Reasoning. Identify the fallacy in each of the following statements. Write your answers in the blanks.

1. Hong Kong is a crowded city because so many people live there.

_____

2. The football team lost three games in a row right after the new coach took over. Therefore, the new coach must not be very good.

_____

3. Many "natural" cereals are full of sugar, but that is okay because sugar is a "natural" ingredient.

_____

4. Roger is really healthy because he gets a great deal of sleep.

_____

5. It's true that I sell used cars, but I prefer to think of them as "antiques."

_____

6. All the programs on television today are either silly or boring.

_____

7. On the day that Ruth didn't wear her lucky ring, she did poorly on an algebra test. Therefore, not wearing the ring must have caused her to have bad luck.

_____

8. Everyone should learn how to use a home computer because using home computers is something that people ought to know how to do.

_____

Improper Appeals to Emotion

The following appeals to emotion are misleading. Therefore, you should learn to avoid them in your own writing and speech and to recognize them in the writing and speech of others.

1. **Snarl words** and **purr words** are words that are used to create negative and positive emotions in the reader or listener.

2. **Irrelevant personal attacks** are attacks on the character of an opponent that have nothing to do with the issue being discussed.

3. **Bandwagon** is the technique of pressuring others to adopt a belief or to take an action simply in order to conform.

4. **Snob appeal** is a kind of reverse bandwagon in which people are encouraged to do not what everyone else is doing but what is done only by a select few.

5. **Transfer** is the technique of trying to get people to associate their feelings about one thing with another, unrelated thing.

6. **Testimonial** is a personal endorsement of an idea or a product. A testimonial is unreliable if the person making the endorsement is not qualified to do so.

Recognizing Improper Appeals to Emotion. Read the following descriptions of situations in which people are using improper emotional appeals. Circle the letter corresponding to the technique being used in each case.

1. A football player who is not a doctor and who knows little about medicine did a commercial in which he said that taking a certain vitamin was the key to good health.

    a. bandwagon   b. irrelevant personal attack   c. snarl words   d. testimonial

2. Candidate Smith met with his opponent to debate foreign policy issues. He spent the entire debate telling the audience that his opponent was not a person to be trusted.

    a. snob appeal   b. transfer   c. irrelevant personal attack   d. testimonial

3. Anne told Malcolm that he should start listening to reggae because that's what everyone is doing.

    a. purr words   b. testimonial   c. transfer   d. bandwagon

4. The magazine advertisements for a certain car always show the car parked in front of mansions or driving through exotic places.

    a. transfer   b. snarl words   c. irrelevant personal attack   d. bandwagon

5. The designer told the audience at the fashion show that her dresses were being worn by the most prominent women in the city.

    a. purr words   b. snob appeal   c. bandwagon   d. testimonial

6. The radio advertisement for a woodburning stove included a description of a "cozy, warm home with the crackle of a blazing fire."

    a. transfer   b. bandwagon   c. purr words   d. snob appeal

7. The campaign office circulated photographs of the candidate surrounded by smiling children.

    a. purr words   b. snob appeal   c. testimonial   d. transfer

Copyright © 1985 by McDougal, Littell & Company

The SQ3R Study Method

One of the most effective methods of studying written material is called **SQ3R**. This method consists of five steps: **S**urvey, **Q**uestion, **R**ead, **R**ecite, and **R**eview. First, you **survey** the material to get a general idea of its content. Then, you prepare a set of **questions** about the material. These may be study questions presented in the book or ones provided by your teacher. They may also be questions that you make up based upon your survey of the selection. Next, you **read** the selection carefully, looking for answers to your questions. Then, you **recite** your answers in your own words and make notes on them. Finally, you **review** the selection to impress the material on your mind.

Using SQ3R. Study the following selection using the SQ3R method. Begin by surveying the material and making a list of study questions. Then, read the selection closely and write the answers to your questions. Write your questions and answers on the lines below.

Folk Ballads

Form. A **folk ballad** is a short, simple, anonymous narrative poem, composed to be sung, and usually following the rhyme scheme a b c b. Many folk ballads contain **choruses**, or **refrains**, which are simply verses that are repeated several times in the course of the song. Folk ballads often make use of repeated phrases that are altered slightly to reflect changes in the story being told.

Content. Folk ballads originated in a time when most people could not read and write. The ballads were therefore passed down orally from generation to generation. The stories told by the ballads were ones that were important to the illiterate folk who created them. Some ballads tell about the deeds of famous heroes such as King Arthur and Robin Hood. Others tell about supernatural events such as the return of a murdered man from the grave. Still others tell about dramatic or important events in people's lives, such as falling in love or going to war.

_____

_____

_____

_____

_____

_____

_____

_____

_____

_____

_____

_____

Types of Test Questions

One way to gain confidence in test-taking is to learn strategies for answering different types of test questions.

1. **Multiple Choice Questions.** You are provided with several possible answers to one question. Read the answers. Then, eliminate the incorrect answers and choose the best answer that remains.

2. **True/False Tests.** You are given several statements and are asked to decide whether each one is true or false. Remember that statements containing words such as *always*, *never*, *all*, or *none* are often false.

3. **Matching Tests.** You are asked to match items in one column with corresponding items in another column. Match the items you are certain about first. Cross out items as you match them.

4. **Completion**, or **Fill-in-the-Blank**, **Tests**. You are asked to fill in gaps in statements given on the test. Make sure your answer fits grammatically into the sentence that you are completing.

5. **Short Answer Tests.** You are asked to answer in one or two short sentences. Answer all parts of the question. Use complete sentences.

6. **Essay Tests.** You are asked to answer in one or more paragraphs. Look for words such as *explain* or *describe* that tell you what to do. Plan your essay before you write. Proofread your completed essay.

Recognizing Types of Test Questions. Match the sample test questions in the left-hand column with the types of test questions in the right-hand column.

_____ 1. The Low Countries include _Belgium_, _Luxembourg_, and _the Netherlands_.

    a. True/False

    b. Multiple choice

    c. Essay

_____ 2. Draw arrows to connect the following authors with their works.

    a. Hawthorne   a. *The Prime of Miss Jean Brodie*

    b. Vonnegut   b. *The Scarlet Letter*

    c. Spark   c. *Slaughterhouse Five*

    d. Completion

    e. Short answer

    f. Matching

_____ 3. When was H. G. Wells born? _Wells was born in 1866._

_____ 4. J. S. Bach composed music for the lute and the harpsichord. _true_

_____ 5. Which of the following are elements of a short story?

    a. plot   c. theme

    b. setting   (d.) all of the above

A **standardized test** is one that allows a person's performance to be compared with that of thousands of others who have taken the test. Important standardized tests include the Preliminary Scholastic Aptitude Test (PSAT), the Scholastic Aptitude Test (SAT), and the American College Testing Program Assessment Test (ACT).

Because standardized tests measure learning and skills gained over a long period of time, cramming is ineffective. The best preparation is to concentrate on improving your language and math skills. Another effective method of preparation is to study the types of questions you are likely to encounter. Two common types of standardized test question are analogies and usage questions.

Analogies are pairs of words that are related in some way. You are given two words that are related to one another. You must find two other words that are related in the same way.

Usage questions require you to recognize writing that does not conform to the rules of standard written English. Common errors in usage questions include incorrect verb tense, improper agreement of pronoun and antecedent, lack of parallel structure, and improper word choice.

Recognizing Analogies. Find the two words that are related to one another in the same way as the two words given in capital letters. Circle the correct answer.

1. **FOOT:LEG::**
   A) feather:bird
   B) hand:arm
   C) beak:hen
   D) body:torso

2. **LUMBER:BUILDING::**
   A) cloth:dress
   B) button:shirt
   C) architect:blueprint
   D) guitar:string

3. **YEAR:DECADE::**
   A) quarter:dollar
   B) penny:dime
   C) penny:nickel
   D) dime:quarter

4. **WORD:SENTENCE::**
   A) brick:wall
   B) window:house
   C) fork:plate
   D) shoe:foot

5. **MAP:DRIVER::**
   A) book:reader
   B) score:conductor
   C) clay:sculptor
   D) dictionary:writer

Recognizing Errors in Usage. Circle the letter that corresponds to the usage error in each sentence. If a sentence is correct as written, circle E, for *No error*.

1. The noise was startling; it's echo reverberated throughout the valley. No error.

2. All the sheep in the herd has been inoculated. No error.

3. Whose going to the library with you and me? No error.

4. Some of the guests are here; their in the family room. No error.

5. I was so exhausted that I laid down and fell asleep immediately. No error.

6. Bella's list of things to do included shopping at the mall, washing the car, and to take the dog for a walk. No error.

7. Each person was well prepared for their part in the performance. No error.

8. Both the dogs and the cat thinks they should have our constant attention. No error.

9. Here's some ideas for building and operating the homecoming float. No error.

10. One of the colors that were chosen for the newly built library is mauve. No error.

How Books Are Classified and Arranged

Fiction. Novels and short story collections are usually arranged in alphabetical order by author. For example, a book by John Steinbeck will be under S.

Nonfiction. Most libraries classify nonfiction books according to the Dewey Decimal System. Books are classified by number in ten major categories, according to their subjects. The ten major Dewey categories are:

000–099	General Works	(includes encyclopedias, references, and almanacs)
100–199	Philosophy	(includes psychology and ethics)
200–299	Religion	(includes theology and mythology)
300–399	Social Science	(includes sociology, economics, and government)
400–499	Language	(includes languages, grammars, and dictionaries)
500–599	Science	(includes mathematics, chemistry, and biology)
600–699	Useful Arts	(includes farming, cooking, sewing, and engineering)
700–799	Fine Arts	(includes music, painting, acting, and photography)
800–899	Literature	(includes poetry, plays, and essays)
900–999	History	(includes biography, travel, and geography)

The major categories are subdivided into many more specific classifications. Each nonfiction book is assigned a number within the major category.

Nonfiction books are arranged on the shelves numerically in order of their classification. Within each classification, books are arranged alphabetically by authors' last names.

Classifying Books. Below are titles and authors of five fiction books. Put them in order as they would appear in the library.

Galactic Warlords by Douglas Hill
Ordinary People by Judith Guest
Deenie by Judy Blume
The Red Pony by John Steinbeck
Durango Street by Frank Bonham

1. _____

2. _____

3. _____

4. _____

5. _____

How the Dewey Decimal System Classifies Information. In what major category would books on the following topics be found?

1. Judaism _____

2. Beethoven's symphonies _____

3. A play by Paul Zindel _____

4. Customs of an Indian tribe _____

5. English as a second language _____

The Card Catalog

The **card catalog** contains alphabetically arranged cards with the call number of each book in the library. There are usually three cards for each book: the **author card**, the **title card**, and the **subject card**. There may also be a **cross-reference card**, referring you to another subject heading in the catalog.

AUTHOR CARD

599	**Mowat, Farley**
	Never Cry Wolf
	Boston, Little Brown, c. 1963
	247 p.

SUBJECT CARD

WOLVES

Mowat, Farley
  Never Cry Wolf
Boston, Little Brown, c. 1963
  247 p.

TITLE CARD

599	**Never Cry Wolf**
	Mowat, Farley
	Never Cry Wolf
	Boston, Little Brown, c. 1963
	247 p.

CROSS-REFERENCE CARD

Wolves
  see also
Animals, Habits and
  Behavior of

Understanding the Card Catalog. Use the following information to make an author card and a title card. Then, on a separate piece of paper, use this information to make a subject card and a cross-reference card.

Author: John William Loughary
Title: *Career and Life Planning Guide*
Subject: Careers
Call number: 650.1

Publisher: Follet Publishing Co.,
　　　　　　　New York, c. 1976
See also: Employment
Number of pages: 180

AUTHOR CARD

TITLE CARD

Using Reference Works (I)

Reference works are tools for obtaining information. Like tools, they should be used in definite ways. Before using any reference work for the first time, skim the preface. The preface will describe how information is organized in the book, provide sample entries, and explain any symbols and abbreviations that the authors of the book have used. The following are some useful reference works:

1. **Dictionaries.** There are three major types of dictionary: unabridged dictionaries, which contain more than 500,000 words each; shorter, abridged dictionaries; and pocket-sized dictionaries. There are also many dictionaries that deal with specific aspects of language, including dictionaries of synonyms and antonyms, slang, rhymes, and clichés.

2. **Encyclopedias.** Encyclopedias are collections of articles on many subjects. The articles are arranged alphabetically. In addition to general encyclopedias such as the *World Book Encyclopedia* and the *Encyclopedia Britannica*, there are many special-purpose encyclopedias that deal with specific subjects such as sports, archaeology, drama, and mathematics.

3. **Almanacs and Yearbooks.** Almanacs and yearbooks are published annually and are useful sources of facts and statistics on current events, government, economics, sports, education, careers, industries, and public service organizations.

4. **Biographical References.** Biographical reference works offer information about the lives of famous people. Some such works deal with specific groups of people such as presidents.

5. **Books About Authors.** A number of biographical reference works, such as *Contemporary Authors* and *Twentieth Century Authors*, deal exclusively with famous writers.

Using Reference Works. Consult the reference works listed in parentheses to tell whether these statements are true or false. Write **T** or **F** after each sentence.

1. The headquarters of the National Basketball Association is located in New York. (almanac) _____

2. President Lyndon Baines Johnson was born in Houston, Texas. (biographical reference) _____

3. Cats were considered sacred in ancient Egypt. (encyclopedia) _____

4. Poet Gwendolyn Brooks won a Pulitzer prize in 1950. (book about authors) _____

5. One meaning of the word *inspiration* is "the act of breathing in." (dictionary) _____

6. Denmark is a constitutional monarchy with a king or queen, a prime minister, and a parliament called a *Folketing*. (encyclopedia) _____

7. In 1982 Buffalo, New York, had a grain storage capacity of 8,200,000 bushels. (almanac) _____

8. A fulmar is "a large sea bird, a member of the eagle family, that lives primarily in tropical climates." (dictionary) _____

Using Reference Works (II)

1. **Literary Reference Books.** There are many valuable reference books that deal with the history of literature, famous quotations and proverbs, the locations of poems and stories, and general information about authors. Some excellent literary reference works include *Bartlett's Familiar Quotations*, *The Oxford Companion to American Literature*, and *Granger's Index to Poetry*.

2. **Pamphlets, Handbooks, and Catalogs.** Many libraries have pamphlets, handbooks, booklets, catalogs, and clippings on a variety of subjects. These are kept in a set of file cabinets called the **vertical file**.

3. **Atlases.** In addition to containing maps, atlases contain other interesting data on a number of subjects. There are even specific subject atlases, such as the *Atlas of World History*, the *Atlas of World Wildlife*, and *Webster's Atlas with Zip Code Directory*.

4. **Magazines.** The *Readers' Guide to Periodical Literature* lists the titles of articles, stories, and poems published in more than one hundred leading magazines. Articles are listed alphabetically under subject and author (and titles when necessary).

Using Reference Works. Answer the following questions using the reference works listed above.

1. What is the title of a recent magazine article on astronomy? In what magazine did this article appear? _____

_____

2. Does your school library have a vertical file? If so, what is the title of one of the works found in this file? _____

_____

3. Who wrote the line "Parting is such sweet sorrow"? _____

4. Which is the largest island in the Hawaiian island chain? _____

5. What is the name of a famous novel by Mary Shelley? _____

6. What is the capital of Portugal? _____

7. What is the real name of the author known as O. Henry? _____

8. Who said, "Give me liberty or give me death"? _____

9. Who wrote the novel *The Haunting of Hill House*? _____

10. Through what country does the Volga river flow? _____

11. What is the title of a recent magazine article on home computers? In what magazine did this article appear? _____

12. Who wrote the poem "The Highwayman"? _____

Review: Using the Library

Using Reference Works. Draw arrows to match the following reference works with the materials to be found in them.

1. Dictionaries   a. Information about authors
2. Literary reference works   b. Information about magazines
3. Atlases   c. Definitions
4. Vertical file   d. Maps
5. Almanacs   e. Facts about current events
6. *Readers' Guide*   f. Pamphlets and handbooks

Locating Materials in the Library. Answer the following questions.

1. What is the name of the system used to classify books in a library?

   _____

2. Explain how nonfiction books are arranged on the library shelves.

   _____

   _____

   _____

3. Explain how fiction books are arranged on the library shelves.

   _____

4. Tell what four types of cards can be found in the card catalog.

   _____   _____

   _____   _____

Finding Materials in Your Library. Write the title of one of each of the following types of works found in your library.

1. A novel _____

2. A dictionary _____

3. An encyclopedia _____

4. An atlas _____

5. A magazine _____

6. An almanac _____

7. A book about painting _____

8. A literary reference work _____

The Forms of Letters

Every business letter has six parts. The **heading** contains, on the first line, your street address; on the second line, your city, state, and ZIP code; and on the third line, the date. The **inside address** contains, on the first line, the person or department that you are writing to; on the second line, the name of the company; on the third line, the street address or post office box number; and on the fourth line, the city, state, and ZIP code. The **salutation** follows the inside address and may be general (*Dear Sir or Madam*:) or specific (*Dear Ms. Garcia*:). The **body** of the letter states your message clearly and concisely. The **closing** follows the body and may be any of the following:

Sincerely,   Yours truly,   Cordially,   Respectfully yours,

Your **signature** is written beneath the closing. Your name is typed under your signature.

Writing a Business Letter. Write a letter to Jerold Kellman, Executive Editor, *Consumer Guide* magazine, and request a test report on a bicycle. Specify the name of the bike you are interested in. The address of the company is 3841 West Oakton Street, Skokie, Illinois 60076.

_____

_____   HEADING

_____

_____

_____   INSIDE ADDRESS

_____

_____   SALUTATION

BODY

_____

_____

_____

_____

_____

_____

_____   CLOSING

_____   SIGNATURE

Requests for Information

One type of business letter that you will write quite often is the **request for information**. This type of letter is used to inquire about employment, college requirements, vacation ideas, or anything else in which you have an interest. The body of the letter should briefly and politely state what information you need and why you need it.

Writing a Letter Requesting Information. Imagine that your class has raised enough money for a class trip. Write to the following address for information on vacations to Yellowstone National Park and the Grand Tetons: Ms. Mary Livingstone, Consumer Service Representative, Grand Travel, Inc., Jackson, Wyoming 83001.

_____

_____ HEADING

_____

_____

_____ INSIDE ADDRESS

_____

_____ SALUTATION

BODY

_____

_____

_____

_____

_____

_____

_____

_____

_____

_____ CLOSING

_____ SIGNATURE

Applications

Fill in the items completely. Print neatly in ink. Read through the entire application before you begin to write. If requested information does not apply to you, write *NA* for "not applicable."

Personal Information

	Date	Social Security Number

Name

Last	First	Middle

Present Address

Street	City	State	Zip

Phone Number   Date of Birth   U.S. Citizen   Yes   No

Employment Desired

Position	Date You Can Start	Salary Desired

Are You Employed Now?   Where?   Duties

Education

	Name and Location of School	Years Attended	Date Graduated	Subjects Studied
Grammar School				
High School				
College or Trade School				

Activities Other Than Religious
(Civic, Athletic, etc.)

Former Employers: *List Below Last Two Employers, Starting with More Recent One.*

Dates	Name and Address of Employer	Salary	Position	Reason for Leaving
From To				
From To				

References: *Give Below the Names of Two Persons Not Related to You, Whom You Have Known at Least One Year.*

Name	Address	Business

List Any Physical Defects   Were You Ever Injured?

In Case of Emergency
Notify

Name	Address	Phone No.

I authorize investigation of all statements contained in this application. I understand that misrepresentation or omission of facts called for is cause for dismissal.

Date   Signature

Résumés

A **résumé** is a list of your experience, education, and skills. Many schools and employers require résumés instead of, or in addition to, applications. Résumés usually include your name, address, and telephone number; your job objective, or goal; a list of your skills; information about your work experiences; information about your education; and the names and addresses of at least two references.

Writing a Résumé. Imagine that you have applied for a job at a local hardware store. The manager of the store wants you to submit a résumé. Use the following worksheet to gather information for this résumé.

Name _____   Telephone _____

Address _____

Job Objective _____

Skills _____

_____

_____

_____

Work Experience (include volunteer work; list each job, starting with the most recent, and give the name and address of the company, dates employed, job title, and duties)

_____

_____

_____

_____

Education (include all schools attended, starting with the most recent; for each school give the name of the school, the address, and any special subjects you have studied)

_____

_____

_____

References (include the names and addresses of two people who will provide good

references for you) _____

_____

_____

_____

Use this information to write a résumé on a separate piece of paper.

Review: Letters, Forms, and Résumés

Writing Business Letters. Use the space below to write the heading and inside address of a letter to a local business requesting an application for employment.

Heading

_____

_____

_____

Inside Address

_____

_____

_____

_____

Filling Out Forms. Complete the following form. If you do not own a dog or cat, create an imaginary one.

Application for Animal License   **PLEASE PRINT**

Name of Owner: _____
                        last   first

Address: _____

_____

Telephone Number: _____ Date: _____

Type of Animal: **DOG** _____   **CAT** _____   **OTHER** _____

Sex of Animal: **MALE** _____   **FEMALE** _____

Has the animal been spayed or neutered? _____

Has the animal been inoculated for rabies? _____

_____

Note: You must include a certificate of inoculation with your application. You must also include a statement verifying that the animal has been spayed or neutered.

The Duties of Group Members

The members of a discussion group have specific duties, as follows:

The **chairperson**, or leader of the discussion, must prepare beforehand by doing some reading and thinking about the subject. During the discussion, he or she must introduce the topic, keep the discussion orderly, give everyone a chance to contribute, and ask questions to keep the discussion moving forward. The chairperson must also take notes on the key points made during the discussion and end the discussion by summarizing what has been said.

The **participants** must take part in the discussion, speak only when recognized by the chairperson, and support their statements with facts, examples, and the opinions of experts. Participants should listen attentively, take notes, and try to understand points of view expressed by other group members.

Preparing for a Discussion. Imagine that a charitable organization has donated three thousand dollars to your school and that this money is to be used for extracurricular activities. You are the chairperson of a group that is to decide how this money will be spent. Prepare for a discussion of this subject by completing the following worksheet.

Topic of the Discussion: _____

_____

Possible Recipients of the Money (clubs and teams in your school): _____

_____

_____

_____

_____

Questions To Keep the Discussion Moving Forward:

1. _____

_____

2. _____

_____

3. _____

_____

4. _____

_____

5. _____

_____

6. _____

_____

Keys to Effective Speaking

Follow these guidelines whenever you rehearse or deliver a speech.

Nonverbal Communication

Dress and Grooming. Dress and groom yourself in a way that will not draw attention away from your speech. Make sure that your clothing is appropriate to the occasion.

Eye Contact. Eye contact will make your audience more receptive and attentive. Scan the entire audience with your eyes. Do not look solely at any one person. If you find it difficult to look your audience members in the eyes, try looking at the tops of their heads.

Poise and Posture. Do not pose; just stand comfortably. Try to appear relaxed and confident. Putting one foot slightly ahead of the other or adopting a wider stance than usual will help you to maintain your balance. Move about, if possible. Do not lean on a lectern or desk except to emphasize a point. Do not slouch.

Gestures and Facial Expressions. These can be very effective to emphasize particular points. A look of concern, for example, can communicate the seriousness of an idea. Avoid planned gestures and expressions. Instead, let these develop naturally from the emotions that you feel with regard to your subject.

Verbal Communication

Volume. Speak loudly enough for your audience to hear you without difficulty, but not so loudly that your audience becomes uncomfortable. Vary your volume for emphasis.

Articulation. Speak a little more precisely than you do in ordinary conversation. Pronounce every syllable of your words clearly and distinctly. Be careful to pronounce final consonants. Do not clip vowel sounds or hold s sounds.

Pace. Speak a little more slowly than is common in ordinary conversation. Speak at a steady rate with some variation for emphasis.

Pitch. Avoid speech that is too high and thin or that is artificially low. Avoid monotony by varying your pitch, slightly exaggerating the natural pitch variations that occur in ordinary conversation.

Pauses. Pause before important points for dramatic effect.

Using Good Speech Skills. Imagine that you have been asked to introduce a visiting celebrity to an audience of students and faculty members at your school. On your own paper, write a short speech introducing this person. Then, practice your speech, bearing in mind the guidelines presented above.

Keys to Effective Listening

Follow these guidelines whenever you listen to other speakers.

Listening Courteously

1. Do not speak when someone else is speaking.
2. Sit upright and direct your attention to the speaker.
3. Give the speaker positive feedback by using appropriate facial expressions and by maintaining eye contact.
4. Listen for main ideas and supporting details in what the speaker is saying.
5. Take notes if appropriate.

Use this checklist whenever you evaluate a speech given by another student.

Checklist for Evaluating Speeches

CONTENT

Introduction
gets audience's attention _____
is brief and to the point _____
is appropriate to the topic _____

Body
supports the main idea _____
contains no irrelevant material _____
states supporting ideas completely _____
develops supporting ideas completely _____

Conclusion
is brief _____
provides a summary of major points or
draws attention back to main idea _____

PRESENTATION

Nonverbal
speaker has good posture _____
speaker is relaxed and confident _____
speaker has good eye contact _____
gestures and facial expressions
are natural and appropriate _____

Verbal
speaker is not too quiet or too loud _____
speaker's articulation is clear _____
speaker's pace is not too slow or too rapid _____
speaker's pitch is not too high or too low _____
speaker varies volume, pace, and pitch _____
speaker uses pauses effectively _____

Using Good Listening Skills. Use the checklist given above to evaluate the quality of a news report on a local television station.

Grammar and Usage

The Noun

A noun is the name of a person, place, thing, or idea.

PERSONS	PLACES	THINGS	IDEAS
girl	town	earth	freedom
Albert Einstein	Central Avenue	pyramid	beauty

A **common noun** is the name of a whole group of persons, places, things, or ideas. A **proper noun** is the name of an individual person, place, thing, or idea, and must begin with a capital letter.

COMMON NOUNS: doctor, city, month
PROPER NOUNS: Dr. Miller, Philadelphia, February

Identifying Nouns. Underline all the nouns in the following sentences.

EXAMPLE: <u>Javier</u> went quickly to the <u>telephone</u> and called the <u>police</u>.

1. Our house was designed by a local architect, Susan Green.

2. The Dewey Decimal System is used to classify books in a library.

3. Either the President or the Vice-President will attend the conference in Geneva.

4. Mark Janezic, our secretary, read the minutes of the meeting.

5. Mrs. Johnson serves in the legislature in Albany.

6. John Hancock signed the Declaration of Independence.

7. My whole family was able to see the Kentucky Derby this year.

8. Bernard likes football but finds baseball too slow.

9. John Adams was our second President.

10. The artist has several paintings at the exhibit this month.

Recognizing Common Nouns and Proper Nouns. In the following sentences, decide which nouns are *proper nouns*. Rewrite them, using capital letters.

EXAMPLE: Every summer he camps near green lake. _____ *Green Lake* _____

1. An award will be presented to dr. licata. _____

2. My sister will soon graduate from indiana university. _____

3. Our friends will leave soon for a tour of italy. _____

4. Maria is now a patient at oakland hospital. _____

5. My pen pal is a girl who lives in france. _____

6. We crossed the mississippi river soon after noon. _____

7. She has never been to australia or new zealand. _____

8. Willie nelson gave a concert at his home in texas. _____

9. Our family visited san francisco last summer. _____

10. Great athletes such as "magic" johnson earn enormous salaries. _____

The Pronoun

A pronoun is a word used in place of a noun. The noun for which the pronoun stands and to which it refers is called its **antecedent.**

Personal Pronouns. Pronouns used in place of people's names are called **personal pronouns.** Personal pronouns are also used to refer to things.

FIRST PERSON (the person speaking):   I, me, my, mine, we, us, our, ours
SECOND PERSON (the person spoken to):   you, your, yours
THIRD PERSON (the person or thing spoken about):   he, she, it, they, his, hers, its, their, theirs, him, her, them

Compound Personal Pronouns. A *compound personal pronoun* is formed by adding *-self* or *-selves* to a personal pronoun, as follows:

FIRST PERSON: myself, ourselves
SECOND PERSON: yourself, yourselves
THIRD PERSON: himself, herself, itself, oneself, themselves

Identifying Personal Pronouns. Underline the personal pronouns. Circle the antecedent of each pronoun and draw an arrow to it.

1. Mr. Black told Kathy that he would give her a summer job in his store.

2. Mr. Di Nicola listens to news reports on the radio, but they sometimes upset him.

3. When the astronomers spotted Halley's comet, it was still a billion miles away.

4. The chef prepared the pepper steak, but it wasn't up to his usual standards.

5. Carlos meant to bring the new flute to rehearsal, but he forgot it.

6. Jane has toured Idaho and Oregon, and they have become her favorite states.

7. Although Elaine is only six years old, she can already use a computer.

8. The pilot checked the fuel supply before he took off again.

9. The club members approved the treasurer's report as soon as they heard it.

10. Jill played her recorder while Lois played her guitar.

Using Compound Personal Pronouns. Find an acceptable compound personal pronoun for each sentence below. Write it in the space. Then draw an arrow to its antecedent.

EXAMPLE: We _ourselves_ will have to do the clean-up work.

1. Mrs. Nosalski built the ham radio by _____.

2. Jane hurt _____ when she fell on the rough gravel in the driveway.

3. The land _____ is full of mystery.

4. The archaeologist blames _____ for the failure of the expedition.

5. We are making the costumes for the spring musical _____.

More About Pronouns

Indefinite Pronouns. Some pronouns do not refer to a definite person or thing. They are called **indefinite pronouns**.

SINGULAR INDEFINITE PRONOUNS

another	anything	either	everything	no one
anybody	one	everyone	neither	someone
anyone	each	everybody	nobody	somebody

PLURAL INDEFINITE PRONOUNS

both   many   few   several

Demonstrative Pronouns. Words like *this*, *that*, *these*, and *those* are used to point out, or demonstrate, which one or ones are meant. They always refer to a definite person or thing. The words they refer to may come later in the sentence or in another sentence altogether.

That is my house. (*house* is the word referred to.)

Interrogative Pronouns. The pronouns *who*, *whose*, *whom*, *which*, and *what* are used to ask questions. When used in this way, they are **interrogative pronouns**.

Who is at the door?   *Which* tape did you buy?

Indentifying Pronouns. Decide whether the pronouns underlined in the following sentences are **A** indefinite, **B** demonstrative, or **C** interrogative.

1. <u>Who</u> wrote the script for the documentary on pueblo life? _____

2. <u>No one</u> knows mathematics better than Mrs. Lebowitz. _____

3. <u>Those</u> are not the only hardships the pioneers endured. _____

4. <u>Each</u> of us wants to do his best during the fund drive. _____

5. <u>That</u> is the pen that Lincoln used to write the *Gettysburg Address*. _____

6. <u>Whom</u> did you see running up the alley? _____

7. <u>Everyone</u> is eager to see the new lion cubs. _____

8. <u>That</u> is the Adler Planetarium over there. _____

9. <u>Neither</u> of those expensive movies did well at the box office. _____

10. <u>Whose</u> comments are these on your paper? _____

11. <u>Few</u> of us know what careers we will pursue in the future. _____

12. <u>This</u> is my favorite computer magazine. _____

13. <u>Whom</u> did you sit by at the variety show? _____

14. There isn't <u>anything</u> left in the cupboard. _____

15. <u>Several</u> of us plan to go to the book sale at the old library building. _____

16. <u>Which</u> of these reference works lists famous quotations? _____

17. <u>This</u> is not the sort of game I enjoy playing. _____

18. <u>Someone</u> offered to paint a mural on the side of the building. _____

The Verb

A verb is a word that expresses an action, condition, or state of being. The verb tells what is happening in the sentence.

An **action verb** tells about doing something: *hope, dream, eat, speak.*

> I *read* many magazines.   Dolores *ate* the taco.

A **linking verb** describes a state of being. It links the subject to an adjective or to another noun or pronoun in the sentence.

> Jim *is* sleepy.   Eileen *was* the announcer.

The word *be* is a linking verb, as are its forms: *am, are, is, was, were, be, been,* and *being.* Other linking verbs are *appear, become, seem, sound, feel, remain, taste,* and *stay.*

> Helen *seems* calm.   The children *remained* quiet.

Some linking verbs become action verbs when they describe the *act* of doing something.

> I *felt* the soft fabric.   Sasha *tasted* the stew.

Identifying Action Verbs and Linking Verbs. In the following sentences, underline each verb. Then write **A** if it is an action verb or **L** if it is a linking verb.

> **EXAMPLE:**   Jane <u>feels</u> confident about her abilities as a dancer.   *L*

1. Salvatore cooked dinner for his entire family. _____

2. The boy seemed restless after the long program. _____

3. The lilacs in the garden smelled wonderful. _____

4. We stayed quiet for an hour after dinner. _____

5. Our dog always strains at its leash. _____

6. Liz Smith pitched for our team in the game yesterday. _____

7. The bananas in this pudding taste overripe. _____

8. Eve is president of the sophomore class. _____

9. The boys appear calm again after all the excitement. _____

10. I play the piano for at least an hour every day. _____

11. This mythical creature ate everything in its path. _____

12. The patient's pulse became more regular during the night. _____

13. The puppy in the veterinarian's office looked lost and forlorn. _____

14. The younger workers grew tired more quickly. _____

15. I tasted the hot soup carefully. _____

16. Farmers in California grow many exotic fruits and vegetables. _____

17. The gorillas in the ape house seem friendly enough. _____

18. Which of the two versions of the song sounds better to you? _____

Main Verbs and Auxiliaries

Many verbs consist of more than one word. They consist of a **main verb** and one or more **auxiliaries**, or helping verbs. A main verb and its auxiliaries are called a **verb phrase**. The last word in the phrase is the main verb.

The most frequently used auxiliaries are the forms of *do*, *be*, and *have*. Other common auxiliaries include the following:

must	may	shall	could	would
might	can	will	should	

AUXILIARY	MAIN VERB	VERB
has	been	has been
is	giving	is giving
should have	played	should have played
could have been	hurt	could have been hurt
was being	used	was being used

Often the parts of a verb are separated by a word or words that are not part of the verb.

We *had* just *arrived*.   He *will* certainly *recognize* us next time.

Identifying the Complete Verb. Underline the main verb and the auxiliary in the following sentences. Do not include any modifiers.

1. The flying lizards of Southeast Asia can glide from tree to tree.

2. Mr. Costello is constantly giving us directions for each step in our work.

3. The campers should have pitched their tent on higher ground.

4. Joe could have been badly injured by that softball.

5. The hobos have actually been forming a union.

6. We will be electing class officers tomorrow.

7. The snowfall had not quite ended at six this morning.

8. I shall certainly miss that class next semester.

9. Over two hundred thousand ocean-dwelling organisms have been identified.

10. For several years, the prices of video recorders have been falling.

11. How many books have you read this year?

12. I have already read the novel twice.

13. According to legend, the swan does not sing until just before it dies.

14. Nancy and Mark have been given major parts in the school play.

15. Eubie Blake was still playing the piano in his ninety-ninth year.

16. Ms. Smith has definitely agreed to our suggestions.

17. The new club officers will have been chosen by tomorrow evening.

18. You could have gone to the principal's office without me.

19. Mr. Davis has never neglected his work before.

20. By the end of the year, she will have been teaching for two decades.

The Adjective

An adjective is a word that modifies a noun or pronoun. The word *modify* means "to change or add to in some way."

Adjectives are used to tell *which one*, *what kind*, *how many*, or *how much* about nouns and pronouns.

WHICH ONE: *this* postcard, *that* store, *these* tires, *those* friends
WHAT KIND: *large* suitcase, *sweet* corn, *dull* program, *beautiful* scene
HOW MANY: *some* apples, *all* cats, *several* choices, *most* students, *five* cars
HOW MUCH: *little* encouragement, *much* help, *plentiful* supply

Three little words—*the*, *a*, and *an*—are called **articles**, not adjectives.

Identifying Adjectives. In the following sentences, underline each adjective. Then circle the word it describes or modifies and draw an arrow to it. Do not underline articles.

EXAMPLE: The old maple is beautiful in the fall.

1. Most new Presidents are cautious when they deal with Congress.

2. The window of the store was full of attractive new clothes.

3. A large trophy is given to the winner of this tough competition.

4. Several small sharks circled in the shallow water.

5. Most humorous plays have serious sides, too.

6. Potters mold moist clay and then bake it in hot ovens.

7. Electronic games are popular among young people.

8. Most people are curious about the future.

9. Because she was energetic, Sally jogged for two hours.

10. Some authors attract the attention of the reader with the first paragraph.

11. These posters were designed by a brilliant artist named Valdez.

12. Black bears sometimes steal supplies from careless campers.

13. H. G. Wells wrote a famous novel, *The Invisible Man*.

14. Three hundred people turned up for the last game of the season.

15. Many students at this school study foreign languages.

16. The empty stage was bathed in a soft, blue light.

17. Medical researchers have not found a cure for the common cold.

18. Little work can be done on this important project until more money has been raised.

19. The long trip on the famous Orient Express took one from Paris to Istanbul.

20. The pyramids of Giza were among the seven wonders of the ancient world.

21. A fierce wind shook the ancient rafters of the house.

22. These yellow apples taste better than those red ones.

The Adverb

An adverb modifies a verb, an adjective, or another adverb. Adverbs tell *where*, *when*, *how*, or *to what extent*.

WHERE: Leave your coat *inside*.
WHEN: She arrived *late*.
HOW: He drove *slowly*.
TO WHAT
EXTENT: The wall was *completely* covered with vines.

Identifying Adverbs. Read the following sentences carefully. Underline each adverb, and draw an arrow to the word or words it modifies. (Don't forget to include auxiliary verbs as well as the main verb.)

EXAMPLE: Mary often arrives early for school.

1. Ursula K. LeGuin's books are widely read and enjoyed.

2. By six o'clock the ground was completely covered with snow.

3. As a diplomat, Ben Franklin was particularly successful.

4. Mr. Jones left his laundry outside in the rain.

5. Nina always works at the gas station after school.

6. Sarah has worked hard for her promotion to assistant manager.

7. Our coach was absolutely certain we would win.

8. Ira reluctantly agreed to accept our nomination.

9. Mara cautiously entered the ice rink.

10. Luisa now speaks English fluently.

11. Our guests arrived early in the morning.

12. Mr. Smith is grading our term papers carefully.

13. My cousin will arrive at O'Hare tonight at six o'clock.

14. Mario patiently demonstrated a complicated macramé knot.

15. The little boy gazed wistfully out the window at the rain.

16. Wait for us outside on the library steps.

17. Tim pedaled more slowly as he approached the intersection.

18. Tyrone confidently gave his speech on the history of motorcycles.

19. Joan always memorizes her part easily.

20. Lance secretly longed to be a hero in the days of King Arthur.

21. My cousins returned to Canada yesterday.

22. Everyone will definitely receive a copy of the book.

23. During the last game, the stands were nearly empty.

24. She is quite sure her information is accurate.

The Preposition

A preposition relates its object to some other word in the sentence.
A preposition never appears alone. It is always used with a word or group of words called its **object**. The preposition and its object make up a **prepositional phrase**.

> Go *into* the house. (*into the house* is a prepositional phrase.)
> Mrs. Jones fell *off* the ladder. (*off* is a preposition; *ladder* is its object.)

Here are some frequently used prepositions:

about	among	beside	except	near	through
above	around	between	for	of	to
across	at	beyond	from	off	under
after	before	by	in	on	up
against	behind	down	into	out	with
along	beneath	during	like	over	without

Identifying Prepositions and Their Objects. Underline each preposition in the following sentences, and draw an arrow to its object. Some of these sentences contain more than one prepositional phrase.

EXAMPLE: Joe left his jacket at my house.

1. It rained hard during the night, but it stopped before dawn.
2. The boy climbed carefully up the tree.
3. Mary and Betty were the best golfers on the team.
4. Darnell planted marigolds among the tomatoes.
5. Our basketball team will play against yours in the playoffs.
6. My grandparents live across the border, in Mexico.
7. Behind the curtain was a reporter from *The Globe*.
8. For six summers I've vacationed in Colorado.
9. What is the name of the game you were playing?
10. The dome above our heads looked like the sky.
11. The mechanic slid beneath the car and checked the oil pan.
12. Have you seen the new dinosaur exhibit at the Field Museum?
13. The Porters live down the street from us.
14. Rachel has ballet and tap lessons after school.
15. The forest ranger noticed a cloud of smoke on the horizon.
16. Amanda waited through the long night at the hospital.
17. Georgia is also the name of a province in the Soviet Union.
18. Phil jumped from the porch onto the grass below.
19. We've lived behind the bakery for ten years.
20. Bethany identified ten varieties of flowers along the river.

The Conjunction

A conjunction is a word that connects words, phrases, or clauses.
Coordinating Conjunctions. The conjunctions that connect similar sentence parts are *and*, *but*, *or*, and *yet*. They are called **coordinating conjunctions.**
Correlative Conjunctions. A few conjunctions are used in pairs: *not only . . . but (also); either . . . or; neither . . . nor; both . . . and; whether . . . or.* These conjunctions are called **correlative conjunctions**.
Conjunctive Adverbs. Certain adverbs are used to join main clauses. Main clauses are groups of words that would otherwise stand alone as separate sentences. Adverbs used in this way are called **conjunctive adverbs**. They are preceded by a semicolon and followed by a comma. Common conjunctive adverbs are these:

accordingly	consequently	however	therefore
also	furthermore	moreover	thus
besides	hence	nevertheless	still

Identifying Conjunctions. Underline the conjunctions in the following sentences.

1. I've studied both French and Spanish in school.

2. Either Laura or Sue will have the lead in the play.

3. Stavros is not only class president but also captain of the football team.

4. Some common plants are poisonous; therefore, they should be kept away from small children.

5. The Loch Ness monster was first sighted in A.D. 565; nevertheless, its existence has not been proved.

6. Both Illinois and Michigan are named for Indian tribes.

7. Whether we hike or go to a movie depends on the weather.

8. Mr. Wilkens has just moved into the state; therefore, he can't vote here.

9. Neither radio nor television offered any good programs last night.

10. The human body contains over two hundred bones, but almost half of these bones are in the hands and feet.

11. In Chinese, the same word means "city" and "wall."

12. I like to play bridge, but I can't keep score.

13. Helen likes to play softball, but her greatest strength is in volleyball.

14. Dan likes to read mysteries and detective stories.

15. English is now one of the most widely spoken languages; however, for about two hundred years, it was not even the official language of England.

16. Both Winston Churchill and Albert Einstein were poor students.

17. Paul Revere was not only a silversmith but also a dentist.

18. Neither Mark Twain nor Robert Frost received a Nobel Prize in literature.

19. Sandy loves to sail, yet he can't swim well.

20. That horse is ten years old; however, I still ride him regularly.

Words Used in Different Ways (I)

Noun or Adjective? A word used to name a person, place, thing, or idea is a noun. The same word may be used before another noun to tell "what kind." When used in this way, the word is an adjective.

> Mary lives in the *village* of Effingham. (noun)
> Our *village* hall was built in 1930. (adjective)

Adjective or Pronoun? A demonstrative pronoun—*this*, *that*, *these*, and *those*—may also be used as an adjective. If the word is used alone in place of a noun, it is a pronoun. If it is used before a noun to tell "which one," it is an adjective.

> *That* is my house. (pronoun)   *That* house is mine. (adjective)

In a similar way, the words *what*, *which*, and *whose* may be used alone as pronouns or before nouns or adjectives.

> *Which* is your house? (pronoun)   *Which* house is yours? (adjective)

Determining How Words Are Used. In the following sentences, decide whether the underlined word is used as a noun or an adjective.

EXAMPLE: That was a wonderful movie. _____ *pronoun* _____

1. Whose car is the shop class repairing? _____

2. Mr. Barnes discussed consumer issues in class this week. _____

3. Product purity is of concern to the consumer. _____

4. Whose dog is that? _____

5. Night games attract a great many people. _____

6. Those postcards show the great pyramid of Cheops. _____

7. Mike served his famous vegetable soup after the hike. _____

8. This is how soap was made in colonial times. _____

9. Do more accidents happen during the day or during the night? _____

10. What driver won the Indianapolis 500 this year? _____

11. What did Sherlock Holmes say to Dr. Watson? _____

12. Many people grow vegetables on vacant city lots. _____

13. Janet made a reference to Harriet Tubman in her report. _____

14. These are the maps we will need for our trip to Florida. _____

15. Which team won the Superbowl? _____

16. What reference books do you keep on your desk? _____

Words Used in Different Ways (II)

Adjective or Adverb? Some words have the same form whether they are used as adjectives or as adverbs. To tell whether a word is used as an adjective or as an adverb, decide what other words in the sentence it goes with, or modifies. If it modifies a noun or a pronoun and tells *which one*, *what kind*, *how many*, or *how much*, it is an adjective.

> Tom is a *fast* runner. (adjective)

If the word modifies any other kind of word and tells *how*, *when*, *where*, or *to what extent*, it is an adverb.

> Tom always runs *fast*. (adverb)

Adverb or Preposition? A number of words may be used either as prepositions or as adverbs. If the word is followed by a noun or pronoun, it is probably a preposition. The noun or pronoun is its object. If the word in question has no object, it is probably an adverb.

> Your shirt is *in* the dryer. (preposition)
> Please let the cat *in*. (adverb)

Determining How Words Are Used. In the following sentences, decide whether the underlined word is used as an adjective, an adverb, or a preposition.

EXAMPLE: We took a <u>slow</u> train to Salt Lake City. _adjective_____

1. The <u>late</u> movie on television last night was *Casablanca*. adj _____
2. The play ends when the curtain comes <u>down</u>. adj _____
3. The Australian finished <u>first</u> in the race. adv _____
4. Mrs. Graves arrived <u>late</u> for the board meeting. adv _____
5. Climb <u>aboard</u>. adv, prep _____
6. The Greeks tricked the Trojans by hiding <u>inside</u> a wooden horse. prep _____
7. Hal and Jim raced <u>down</u> the hill. adv _____
8. Wally pulled his belt <u>tightly</u> around him. adv _____
9. Several people have gone <u>over</u> the edge of Niagara Falls and survived. prep _____
10. The <u>first</u> television transmission was in the 1920's. adv _____
11. The excited children knew that the piñata had candy <u>inside</u>. _____
12. The Kesslers always go <u>south</u> for the winter. _____
13. He spoke so <u>low</u> that I could hardly hear him. _____
14. The dress is too <u>tight</u> for Mary. _____
15. Can you tell that I've never played tennis <u>before</u>? _____

The Infinitive

There are a number of highly useful words in English that are difficult to classify as parts of speech. These are **infinitives**, **gerunds**, and **participles**. They are called **verbals** because all of them are formed from verbs although they are not verbs themselves. Usually, the infinitive is preceded by "to." The kinds of infinitives are as follows:

ACTIVE PRESENT:	to give, to ask
PASSIVE PRESENT:	to be given, to be asked
ACTIVE PERFECT:	to have given, to have asked
PASSIVE PERFECT:	to have been given, to have been asked

The infinitive may be used as a noun, an adjective, or an adverb.

NOUN:	*To see* is to believe.
ADJECTIVE:	This is the book *to read*.
ADVERB:	The tickets were hard *to sell*.

Identifying Infinitives. Underline the infinitive in each sentence.

1. It takes seventeen muscles to smile.

2. To be a ballet dancer requires years of strenuous practice.

3. A superb swimmer, the penguin is unable to fly.

4. Was Leif Ericson the first Norwegian sailor to discover America?

5. Mr. Lopez decided to paint his den this weekend.

6. Lorraine taught Stewart to play golf.

7. We intend to visit the Children's Museum in Boston.

8. Raoul seems to have practiced his free throws.

9. To write down your objectives is the first step.

10. Lynn's ambition is to be a lawyer.

11. My parents have gone to Detroit to visit relatives.

12. Bridget had to prime the wood before she could paint it.

13. John listened carefully to get all the directions.

14. To be a writer was young Anne Frank's goal.

15. Dr. Livingstone left home to become an explorer.

16. We are all trying to help the refugees.

17. That is a difficult question to answer.

18. It is dangerous to swim outdoors during a thunderstorm.

19. Many people like to sleep late on Saturday morning.

20. My sister is planning to marry Ralph in June.

21. Jacques and Joseph Montgolfier were the first people to ride in a hot air balloon.

22. Be careful not to look directly at the sun during an eclipse.

The Gerund

The **gerund** is a verbal noun that always ends in -*ing*. It is used in almost every way that a noun can be used.

Wheezing is a symptom of asthma. (subject of the verb)
I like *fishing*. (object of the verb)
She is an authority on *gardening*. (object of the preposition)

Identifying Gerunds. Find the gerunds in the sentences below. Draw a line under each gerund. Remember to look for the -*ing* ending.

EXAMPLE: Rising early is hard for me.

1.   I don't mind missing breakfast today.
2.   Laughing sometimes helps sick people recover more quickly.
3.   Larry's specialty is making omelettes.
4.   Hiking is a popular form of recreation in Europe.
5.   Sally enjoys solving riddles and puzzles.
6.   Excessive dieting can endanger your health.
7.   Getting the lead in the play was all Meg thought of.
8.   After jogging five miles we took a long rest.
9.   I like playing the zither.
10.   Taking blood samples is the job of a phlebotomist.
11.   Mr. Jones teaches organic gardening to members of the 4-H Club.
12.   Let's stop worrying about the matter if we can.
13.   Cleaning my room on weekends is not my idea of fun.
14.   Practicing judo takes most of Peter's free time.
15.   In Greek mythology, Charon was given the job of ferrying souls to the afterlife.
16.   Good acting is always a pleasure to see.
17.   Working out every other day gives your muscles a chance to recuperate.
18.   Have you tried resting a bit after dinner?
19.   Collecting stamps is Art's favorite hobby.
20.   After organizing his notes carefully, Luis gave an excellent speech.
21.   Sleeping occupies about one third of a person's lifetime.
22.   Camping in the mountains is Booker's idea of a perfect vacation.
23.   Training for the Olympics requires great dedication.
24.   A short rest now will keep you from becoming too tired later.
25.   Reading a good mystery is a perfect way to spend an afternoon.

The Participle

The **participle** is a verbal that is used as an adjective to modify a noun or a pronoun. The forms of the participle are these:

PRESENT PARTICIPLE:	asking
PAST PARTICIPLE:	asked
PERFECT PARTICIPLE:	having asked
PASSIVE PERFECT PARTICIPLE:	having been asked

Identifying Participles. In each sentence below, underline the participle (or participles). Draw an arrow to the word that the participle modifies.

EXAMPLE: Sobbing, the little boy looked for his lost toy.

1. Jumping up and down, the cheerleaders led us in the school yell.

2. The *Ninth Symphony* is one of Beethoven's most inspiring works.

3. We heard the speech given by the congresswoman.

4. Lucinda spent hours in the pool, drifting lazily on a raft.

5. Did you notice the skateboard lying in the driveway?

6. The star was in the wings, repairing his costume.

7. Exhausted after his long hike, Dave flopped down on the step.

8. The Nobel Prizes, given each year since 1901, will be awarded again this year.

9. Wandering aimlessly along the beach, the little boy picked up the shells and dropped them in his bucket.

10. Mike, having spent all his money on lunch and dinner, wasn't able to buy a book.

11. Holding on to the railing, the patient slowly climbed the stairs.

12. Did you notice the raccoon sitting in that tree?

13. We read several poems written by Emily Dickinson.

14. The Senator, irritated by my question, refused to answer.

15. Julia, hearing the footsteps outside the door, looked at me nervously.

16. My cousin, amused by the beginning of the television program, sat back to watch it all.

17. Prized as valuable gems, diamonds are a form of carbon.

18. Thomas Jefferson, considered one of our greatest Presidents, was born in Virginia.

19. Blinded by childhood glaucoma, Ray Charles nevertheless became a famous jazz musician.

20. Having been given our directions, we began to work on the project.

21. Those creatures jumping from branch to branch are spider monkeys.

22. Falling through the atmosphere, the meteorite rapidly burned away.

Review: The Classification of Words

Identifying Parts of Speech. Tell whether the italicized word in each sentence is a noun, pronoun, verb, adjective, adverb, preposition, or conjunction.

EXAMPLE: The *gladiolas* were a beautiful shade of yellow. _____*noun*_____

1. The grandfather *clock* dates back to the eighteenth century. _____n_____

2. One of the first coins made in Massachusetts *was* the oak tree shilling. _verb_

3. I wish I had *more* spending money. _adj._

4. Buddy polishes *his* car every weekend. _pronoun_

5. It is very hot in the sun, *but* it is pleasant in the shade. _conj_

6. The pilot was *seriously* injured in the crash. _adv._

7. *Everyone* should know how to administer first aid. _noun_

8. I threw my dirty clothes *down* the laundry chute. _prep._

9. The volunteers in the hospital *distribute* newspapers and mail. _v._

10. The van was so *dirty* we couldn't tell what color it was. _adj._

Identifying Verbals. In the following sentences, determine whether the italicized word is a gerund, participle or infinitive. Mark **G**, **P**, or **I** on the blank after the sentence.

EXAMPLE: The *winding* road was dark. _P_

1. Computer management is a *growing* field. _G_

2. Ken's goal is *to run* in the New York City Marathon. _I_

3. We photographed the dolphins *swimming* alongside our boat. _G_

4. *Speaking* before the class terrifies some students. _I_

5. Camels are able *to drink* a hundred quarts of water in ten minutes. _I_

Using Words in Different Ways. In the following sentences, decide how the italicized word is used. Choose from: verbs, noun, adverb, preposition, pronoun, adjective.

EXAMPLE: *This* outline will help me study for the test. _adjective_

1. Do you like *this*? _n_

2. Victoria *ruled* England until her death in 1901. _v._

3. We had to use *ruled* paper for our compositions. _adj._

4. Because of gravity, things fall *down*, instead of up. _P._

5. Tanya's *down* jacket kept her quite warm. _adj._

What Is a Sentence?

A sentence is a group of words that expresses a complete thought.

INCOMPLETE: The girl in the beret. (What about her?)
COMPLETE: The girl in the beret is my sister.

INCOMPLETE: Tired after a long day of hiking. (Who was tired?)
COMPLETE: I was tired after a long day of hiking.

INCOMPLETE: Before the game was over. (What happened?)
COMPLETE: Before the game was over, the rain began.

Recognizing Sentences. Read each group of words carefully. If the words form a complete sentence, write **C** in the blank. If the words do not form a complete sentence, write **N** in the blank.

EXAMPLE: When Mark crossed the street ___*N*___

1. Dolores throwing a ball _____

2. Mary Ann loves Latin class _____

3. Ken was startled when the lizard leaped at him _____

4. In the dungeon of the castle _____

5. Please be on time for the meeting _____

6. Beth's favorite city is San Francisco _____

7. Ms. Gomez, a stockbroker for the last two years _____

8. After waving to me, Bob turned the corner _____

9. Here comes our train _____

10. The oldest civilization on earth _____

11. The buffet table was loaded with tempting food _____

12. A tall man wearing a brown suit and a Panama hat _____

13. Sandra Day O'Conner, a Supreme Court Justice _____

14. Frightened by the sound of footsteps outside the window _____

15. The boys are looking forward to wind surfing next summer _____

16. Moreover, the speaker's main point _____

17. Becoming irritated by our questions _____

18. Robin Hood, the legendary outlaw of Sherwood Forest _____

19. Mrs. Smith drove carefully through the heavy traffic _____

20. Mr. Grant works in the garden every day _____

Kinds of Sentences

Sentences may be classified according to the purpose of the speaker or writer:

1. The **declarative sentence** is used to make a statement of fact, wish, intent, or feeling. It is followed by a period.

    I have seen that movie twice.   I wish I could go on the picnic.

2. The **imperative sentence** is used to state a command, request, or direction. The subject is always *You*, even though it may not be expressed in the sentence. It is usually followed by a period.

    (You) Be on time for dinner.   (You) Open the window, please.

3. The **interrogative sentence** is used to ask a question. It is always followed by a question mark.

    Do you have a new sweater?   Which soccer ball is yours?

4. An **exclamatory sentence** is used to express strong feeling. It is always followed by an exclamation point.

    Don't burn yourself!   How lucky you are!   Keep out!

Classifying Sentences. Read the following sentences and decide the classification of each. Place the number that corresponds to each sentence category in the blank.

    EXAMPLE: Susan is a senior. ___1___

1. If only I could go to Colorado this summer! ___1___
2. Please buckle your seat belt. ___2___
3. The Vice-President will visit Egypt next week. ___1___
4. What are sweetbreads made from? ___3___
5. The saxophone was invented by Antoine Joseph Sax. ___1___
6. Do you know how to convert Fahrenheit to Celsius? ___3___
7. Ouch! I burned my finger! ___4___
8. Turn left at the second stop sign. ___2___
9. San Marino is the smallest republic in Europe. ___1___
10. Initial the top right-hand corner of each sheet of paper. ___2___
11. Richard Martin's short stories have appeared in many magazines. _____
12. Have you ever read *The Red Badge of Courage*? _____
13. You can't be serious! _____
14. Meet me at seven o'clock in front of the library. _____
15. Why does Becky look so mysterious? _____
16. Soft-shoe is tap dancing done without taps on the shoes. _____
17. I told you so! _____
18. Do you attend the concerts given by the Cleveland Symphony Orchestra? _____

Subject and Predicate

The two essential parts of every complete sentence are the subject and the predicate. The **subject** is the person, thing, or idea about which something is said. The **predicate** tells something or asks something about the subject.

SUBJECT	PREDICATE
Children	played.
The three children	played in the sandbox.
Girls	sing.
Both girls	sing in the glee club and chorus.

The Simple Predicate or Verb. In every predicate, the most important word is the **verb**. The simple predicate of the sentence is the verb.

The verb may be a phrase consisting of more than one word: *have sung*, *might have gone*. When parts of the verb are interrupted by a modifier, the modifier is *not* part of the verb: *were* not *lost*, *did* not *seem*.

Identifying the Subject and Verb. Underline the verb in each of the following sentences. Draw a circle around each subject.

EXAMPLE: (Mary) cautiously <u>opened</u> the door.

1. Miss Williams is going to Baton Rouge tomorrow.
2. Jackie Robinson was the first black player in major league baseball.
3. Our class chartered a bus for the trip.
4. I have never really understood why people enjoy those programs.
5. The Ferons have played eighteen holes of golf today.
6. The students had never finished their work so quickly before.
7. Miners have always had a dangerous job.
8. Diana has been working at a delicatessen.
9. After his long flight, Miguel was very tired.
10. The bridge was never completed.
11. Aunt Helen has just arrived for a week's visit.
12. In biology class Shelly carefully dissected an earthworm.
13. The witness answered the questions simply and directly.
14. Our team has never beaten yours.
15. Today, many adults are wearing braces on their teeth.
16. Johanna has never visited the South.
17. Mr. Gonzales often walks his dog in the evening.
18. Mother's Day is celebrated on the second Sunday in May.
19. *Animal Farm* is one of my favorite books.
20. Uncle Ted will prepare Thanksgiving dinner for fourteen people.

Subjects in Unusual Positions

In most sentences, the subject appears before the verb. In some sentences, however, this order is reversed.

Questions. In most questions beginning with interrogative words such as *where*, *when*, *why*, *how*, *how much*, the subject falls between parts of the verb.

How does he look?   When will the game begin?

In questions beginning with *who* or *what*, the verb may follow the subject in normal order.

Who saw it?   What is happening here?

Sentences Beginning with *There* and *Here*. In such sentences, the subject usually follows the verb.

There are the posters.   Here is your jacket.

Sentences in Inverted Order. For emphasis or variety of style, the subject is sometimes placed after the verb.

Strolling down the busy street was an escaped lion.

Identifying Subjects and Verbs. Underline the verb in each sentence below. Circle the subject.

EXAMPLE: By the road stood a (porter) in uniform.

1. Why does the sky look blue?

2. From Virginia have come many of our Presidents.

3. Here is a map of Saudi Arabia.

4. What are you doing New Year's Eve?

5. There is the best passer on the team.

6. How much does a sandwich cost at that restaurant?

7. At the top of the stairs stood Dolly Levi.

8. From the little girl came a drawn-out sigh.

9. Up the side of the mountain climbed the sure-footed goats.

10. When will you be coming through Atlanta?

11. From the beach came the sounds of the surf.

12. Where is Cliff going on his vacation?

13. Driving cautiously down the street was my Uncle Craig.

14. Among the celebrities at the benefit was Michael Jackson.

15. Why did Pandora open that box?

16. Charging rapidly toward me was an angry bull.

The Direct Object

The **direct object** is a word or group of words to which the verb carries the action from the subject.

Verbs with direct objects are called **transitive verbs**.

I unlocked the *trunk*. (*unlocked* what?)
Dave has studied *Spanish*. (*has studied* what?)

A direct object tells *whom* or *what* after the verb. If a word tells *how*, *when*, *where*, or *why*, it is an adverb.

Ann walked *slowly*. (*slowly* tells how; it is an adverb.)
Bears eat *berries*. (*berries* tells what; it is a direct object.)

Identifying Direct Objects. Underline the verb or verb phrase in each of the following sentences. Circle the direct object of the verb. Do not include modifiers.

EXAMPLE: Jane gave a birthday present to Kate.

1. The candidate made many promises during the campaign.
2. To my horror, I lost my voice before the play.
3. Allan arranged the spices alphabetically on the shelf.
4. Myra Hayes reviews movies for the local paper.
5. Rhoda has a theory about life on other planets.
6. Cara raked the leaves into an enormous pile.
7. Who hit the ball through Mr. Brown's window?
8. We visited a farm in Kentucky during spring vacation.
9. Clyde Tombaugh discovered Pluto in 1930.
10. Dad bought a desk from the antique dealer.
11. Have you changed the water in the aquarium?
12. Jane raised three heifers this spring.
13. The Clarks are having a garage sale on Friday.
14. The telephone awakened everyone in the house.
15. Have you ever read *A Wrinkle in Time*, by Madeleine L'Engle?
16. Pam has not made a decision about her job.
17. Have you paid the fine for these overdue library books?
18. The President's joke lessened the tension at the conference.
19. Lisa discovered several orchids down by the river.
20. The scientists reported the results of their experiment.
21. The sailors dropped the anchor overboard.
22. Please water the plants on the window sill.

The Indirect Object

The **indirect object** of the verb tells *to* or *for whom*, or *to* or *for what*, something is done.

Tell *me* a story.   Show *Brett* your notebook.

A verb has an indirect object *only* if it also has a direct object. The words *to* and *for* are never placed before an indirect object. When followed by a noun or pronoun, *to* and *for* are always prepositions.

Helen told *Sue* a joke. (*Sue* is the indirect object.)
Helen told a joke to *Sue*. (*Sue* is the object of the preposition.)

Identifying Indirect Objects. Underline the indirect object in each of the following sentences. Do not include any direct objects.

EXAMPLE: Bill lent Howard his jacket.

1. Lisa told the children about an elephant.
2. Give me one good reason for doing that job!
3. Pat told us nothing about her change of plans.
4. The United States awarded Audie Murphy the Congressional Medal of Honor.
5. Alberto told me his new address over the phone.
6. Walt Disney gave the world many memorable cartoon characters.
7. I'll send you a copy of the receipt.
8. Mrs. Barnes promised Chris a reward for finding her briefcase.
9. Please show me the best way to upholster a chair.
10. Norman brought us some avocados for the salad.
11. The mayor awarded Joy a plaque for her bravery.
12. I wish you great success at the basketball tournament.
13. Mr. Brent showed Sam his flower garden.
14. Mrs. Todd promised me a reward for finding her dog.
15. Mr. Jordan taught the class the French national anthem.
16. I'll sing you a song from the 1930's.
17. Grandfather told me a story about his boyhood in Poland.
18. I gave the secondhand shop my used clothing.
19. The company president presented Mom a watch at her retirement party.
20. The trainer lent Joel a book about horses.
21. An audience member handed the magician a scarf.
22. Lamonte wrote us a letter from Mexico.
23. To illustrate his point, the teacher drew the class a diagram.
24. The librarian found us a copy of the article.

Predicate Words

A linking verb connects its subject to a word in the predicate. The word that is connected to the subject by a linking verb is called a **predicate word**. There are three types of predicate words: the **predicate noun**, the **predicate pronoun**, and the **predicate adjective**.

> Our math teacher is *Ms. Carson*. (predicate noun)
> That guitar is *his*. (predicate pronoun)
> This puzzle is *impossible*! (predicate adjective)

Identifying Predicate Words. Underline the subjects once and the linking verbs twice. Write the predicate words.

EXAMPLE: Selma's <u>editorial</u> <u><u>was</u></u> extremely effective. *effective*

1. Susan is always very sure of herself. _____

2. The winner of the contest was she. _____

3. That big black dog in the back yard is mine. _____

4. Clerks in the Mason Department Store are usually very helpful. _____

5. The speaker at the meeting was Barbara Walters. _____

6. This homemade chili tastes wonderful! _____

7. Ann feels miserable because of her bad cold. _____

8. Laura's ghost costume looked scary. _____

9. Langston Hughes is my favorite poet. _____

10. Henry VIII became king at the age of seventeen. _____

11. I felt tired after lifting weights at the gym. _____

12. The governor is very modest about her achievements. _____

13. The Grahams' house is a bungalow. _____

14. Mr. Beck's cherry pie tasted delicious. _____

15. My brother is a singer at the San Francisco Opera. _____

16. That is the most valuable coin in my collection. _____

17. Inés seemed anxious during the auditions. _____

18. My chemistry teacher is Mr. Harrison. _____

19. To a casual observer, Jeff's room appears messy. _____

20. Mary Cassatt is famous for her paintings of mothers and children. _____

Compound Parts of Sentences

Subjects, verbs, objects, and predicates may all be compound. That is, they may include more than one part *of the same kind*. The parts are joined by a conjunction.

1. **COMPOUND SUBJECT:**   Ten *girls* and twelve *boys* made up the track team.
2. **COMPOUND VERB:**   The old car *sputtered* and *stopped*.
3. **COMPOUND DIRECT OBJECT:**   He grows *lettuce* and *tomatoes* in his garden.
4. **COMPOUND INDIRECT OBJECT:**   Jeff offered *Mary* and *me* his tickets.
5. **COMPOUND OBJECT OF PREPOSITION:**   Mr. Todd wrote an article on the *movie* and its *director*.
6. **COMPOUND PREDICATE WORD:**   Elliott looks *thoughtful* and *sad*.
7. **COMPOUND PREDICATE:**   I've already *dusted the furniture* and *swept the floors*.

Identifying Compound Parts of Sentences. Look at the italicized words in each sentence below. From the list above, decide what kind of compound the words are. Put the corresponding number in the blank.

EXAMPLE: The girls were *happy* but *subdued*. ___6___

1. The zookeeper left some food for the *chimpanzees* and *gorillas*. _____

2. Liz's favorite old movies feature *Laurel* and *Hardy*. _____

3. Mr. Bennett ordered three *shirts* and two *ties* from the catalog. _____

4. The last two states to join the union were *Alaska* and *Hawaii*. _____

5. Sam is exhausted; he *has jogged* and *bicycled* all day. _____

6. Erica visited *Maine* and *Vermont* last year. _____

7. *Similes* and *metaphors* are common poetic devices. _____

8. The same actor played the roles of *Dr. Jekyll* and *Mr. Hyde*. _____

9. *Chippewa* and *Tillamook* are American Indian languages. _____

10. Dick *studied his history assignment* and *did his math problems*. _____

11. *Newsweek* and *People* are two of my favorite magazines. _____

12. Ms. Thomas questioned *Marco* and *Tim* about their project. _____

13. *Davy Crockett* and *Jim Brown* both died at the Alamo. _____

14. The children *played hopscotch* and *jumped rope*. _____

15. Please tell *Mother* and *Father* Mr. Spencer's question. _____

16. The architect studied the *design* and *construction* of the old house. _____

17. The children laughed at the antics of *Ernie* and *Bert*. _____

18. Mr. Schaeffer spent all his savings for his *house* and *car*. _____

19. The principal gave *Tim* and *Mike* some sound advice. _____

20. Mrs. Storms *read How Green Was My Valley* and *wrote a review of it*. _____

The Prepositional Phrase

A **phrase** is a group of words without a subject and a verb, used as one part of speech. A **verb phrase** is two or more words used as a verb: *has gone*, *should have given*, *could have seen*. A **noun phrase** is two or more words used as a noun: *the Berlin Wall*, *Central Park*.

The **prepositional phrase** consists of the preposition, its object, and modifiers of the object. The object of a preposition is a noun, a pronoun, or a group of words used as a noun.

The **adjective phrase** always comes immediately after the noun or pronoun it modifies.

> My check *for the electronics kit* is in the mail. (*for the electronics kit* modifies *check*.)

The **adverb phrase** tells *how*, *when*, *where*, or *to what extent* about a verb, adjective, or adverb.

> Alex fell *on the icy sidewalk*. (*on the icy sidewalk* tells *where* he fell.)

Identifying Prepositional Phrases. Underline the prepositional phrases in the following sentences. Circle the word or words that each phrase modifies.

> EXAMPLE: The girl in the yellow dress is my cousin from San Diego.

1. We visited the park between rain showers.

2. Mark Spitz won seven gold medals in the 1976 Olympics.

3. The longest-running show on Broadway was *A Chorus Line*.

4. The dog waited patiently under the table.

5. Reporters from the *Courier-Journal* covered the story.

6. Behind the counter stood the worried clerk.

7. Scotland Yard is the headquarters of the London police.

8. Our hockey team will play against yours tomorrow night.

9. The tall man with Gil is Mr. Mendez.

10. The football bounced off the goalpost.

11. Ms. Garner dropped the sliced vegetables into the wok.

12. The heat produced by the sun is tremendous.

13. The title of the novel was *The Time Machine*.

14. Our house is located beyond the city limits.

15. Throughout the night the doctor stayed nearby.

16. Maria fell off the ladder and sprained her ankle.

17. The hull of the ship struck the tip of an iceberg.

18. We are proud because we stayed within our budget.

19. The temperature in the Alaskan village finally climbed above zero.

20. One painting by Joseph Turner sold for six million dollars.

The Infinitive Phrase

The **infinitive phrase** usually begins with the word *to*. The phrase consists of *to*, the infinitive, its complements, and its modifiers.

> Carla wants *to be a lawyer*.
> (The infinitive phrase is the object of *wants*.)

> *To win at chess* requires much concentration.
> (The infinitive phrase is the subject.)

> Milo was glad *to be invited to the party*.
> (The infinitive phrase modifies the adjective *glad*.)

Identifying Infinitive Phrases. Underline the infinitive phrase in each of the following sentences.

EXAMPLE: Joe intends to work hard.

1. To sit through a long movie is impossible for Elliot.

2. Does Joan have enough determination to be a gymnast?

3. Always try to proofread your paper before you turn it in.

4. A running lion is able to reach a speed of sixty miles per hour.

5. The Harlow twins came to play with my little brother.

6. Would you like to discuss the problem with me?

7. Juan will be happy to give you a ride home.

8. To be safe, stay on the bicycle path.

9. Fred was frightened to be alone in the old house.

10. Our plan is to visit Southern California.

11. To be a doctor is Danuta's goal.

12. In her crafts class, Megan learned how to make a quilt.

13. Did you have time to feed the kittens?

14. Mr. and Mrs. Taylor plan to join the Peace Corps together.

15. President Lyndon Johnson declined to run for reelection.

16. Adam tries to do his best for the team.

17. Sarah wanted to paint the ceiling of her room.

18. People are beginning to recognize the problem of acid rain.

19. The lecturer was asked to speak for half an hour.

20. To play tennis every day is Aaron's ambition for the summer.

21. Many Americans have attempted to climb Mt. Everest.

22. In biology class we learned to identify several microscopic organisms.

The Participial Phrase

The **participial phrase** is always used as an adjective phrase to modify a noun or pronoun. It includes the participle together with its modifiers and its complements. Participles usually end in *-ing*, *-ed*, *-d*, *-t*, or *-en*.

Walking rapidly, we reached the town in fifteen minutes.

Annoyed by the noise, the students moved to a quieter part of the library.

The vase, *broken beyond repair*, was discarded.

Having won every game but one, Michigan led the Big Ten.

Identifying Participial Phrases. Underline the participial phrase. Draw an arrow to the word that the participle modifies.

EXAMPLE: Mr. Flynn, annoyed by his secretary's question, answered impatiently.

1.   Having worked overtime all week, Dad was exhausted.

2.   Concerned with safety, I put reflectors on my bike.

3.   Climbing slowly, we approached the top of the hill.

4.   Having soaked the seeds with water, Eddie waited for them to sprout.

5.   Phil, worn out by his long trip, slept for twelve hours last night.

6.   Watching me closely, the dog came toward me.

7.   Encouraged by her past success, Tanya entered the swimming competition again.

8.   Having been hurt in the first game, Al sat on the bench for the rest of the season.

9.   The plates, brought from Denmark by my grandmother in 1930, are on display in a hutch in the dining room.

10.   This pudding made with cornmeal and molasses is a New England dish.

11.   Gelatin, extracted from animal bones and hooves, has many uses.

12.   The students, waiting for the play to begin, looked around the audience.

13.   Working hard all day, the boys finished the job by dinner time.

14.   Driven from their homelands for various reasons, many people each year seek refuge in the United States.

15.   Invented in 1790, wrist watches weren't popular until a century later.

16.   The basketball team, having suffered several injuries, lost in the finals.

17.   Having started before the gun, Kate was disqualified.

18.   We watched Ellie racing to the finish line.

19.   Having been told of her job offer, Kathy smiled happily.

20.   Having spent the afternoon at the beach, Alicia was hot and tired.

21.   Walking through the park, I saw three squirrels and a chipmunk.

22.   Filmed in Saudi Arabia, this movie presents a vivid picture of Arabian customs.

The Gerund Phrase

The **gerund phrase** consists of the gerund, which always ends in *-ing*, and its modifiers and complements. The gerund phrase is *always* used as a noun.

> *Driving a car* takes concentration.
> (The gerund phrase is the subject of the verb *takes*.)

> Vernon finished *painting the ceiling*.
> (The gerund phrase is the direct object of *finished*.)

> After *cleaning for two hours*, we stopped to cook lunch.
> (The gerund phrase is the object of the preposition *after*.)

Identifying Gerund Phrases. Underline the gerund phrases in the sentences below.

EXAMPLE: Brisk walking is Don's favorite exercise.

1. The firefighter received a medal for saving the child's life.

2. Ms. Norman enjoys jogging after work.

3. I remember promising Steve my old bike.

4. Standing during a two-hour train trip is not my idea of relaxation.

5. Do you like working at the supermarket?

6. Volunteering at the hospital is just one of Helen's activities.

7. Ms. Brent enjoys watching quiz shows on television.

8. Scrambling eggs over a fire is my favorite camping task.

9. Taking out the garbage is a daily job around the house.

10. Understanding a foreign language and speaking it well are two different skills.

11. The Thompsons reduced their fuel bills by installing a woodburning stove.

12. Collecting coins is a popular hobby among people of all ages.

13. Sending a letter is one way of keeping in touch with friends.

14. Don't you ever get tired of doing your exercises?

15. The attorney helped his client by winning the jury's sympathy.

16. Julio sings while strumming the guitar.

17. Arguing with me takes much of my little brother's time.

18. Building a picnic table is Allison's winter project.

19. Harvesting the corn will take all day.

20. After standing behind the counter all day, Jim likes to relax at night.

21. Collecting autographs is an interesting hobby.

22. Before entering the radioactive area, the workers donned protective clothing.

23. Roger loves reading about European cities.

24. Sarah memorized the story by reading it over and over again.

The Appositive Phrase

An **appositive** is a word placed after another word to explain or identify it. It is *always* a noun, a pronoun, or another part of speech acting as a noun. The word it explains is *also* a noun, a pronoun, or another part of speech acting as a noun.

My uncle, *a Sioux chief*, is visiting us.
My teacher, *Ms. Marshall*, is very helpful.

An **appositive phrase** consists of the appositive and its modifiers, which may themselves be phrases.

My radio, *an old portable*, is in the repair shop.
(The appositive phrase identifies *radio*. The adjective *old* modifies *portable*.)
The boys climbed the mountain, *one of the highest in the West*. (The appositive phrase identifies *mountain*. The prepositional phrases *of the highest* and *in the West* modify *one*.)

Identifying Appositive Phrases. Underline the appositive phrase in each of the following sentences.

EXAMPLE: Our house, a brick bungalow, is on Oak Street.

1. Mozambique, a country on the southeast coast of Africa, has excellent harbors.

2. Jane made the salad, a tossed one with French dressing.

3. My grandmother, a talented woman, taught me how to cane a chair.

4. The Fates, three goddesses in Greek mythology, controlled human destiny.

5. Biology, Nina's favorite subject, is easy for her.

6. Jerry is visiting in Peoria, his old home town.

7. Mr. and Mrs. Miller, our neighbors for the past eight years, are moving to Dallas.

8. Have you ever read *The Pearl*, the short novel by John Steinbeck?

9. Groucho Marx, the star of many film comedies, also had his own television show.

10. Paella, a Spanish dish, is made from rice, chicken, and seafood.

11. The poem, one of Robert Frost's best, is called "The Death of the Hired Man."

12. I can't find my notebook, the one with my history notes in it.

13. Dick's new suit, a gray flannel one, makes him look much older.

14. Suffrage, the right to vote, was granted to American women in 1920.

15. The theater, a landmark building, is rarely crowded.

16. Knute Rockne, the famed football coach, was born in Norway.

17. The dodo, an awkward flightless bird, has been extinct since 1700.

18. My sister, a graduate of the University of Iowa, is now studying law.

19. Ann Landers, the advice columnist, has a twin sister.

20. Ms. Norbert, the president of the company, will speak at the dinner.

Review: The Parts of a Sentence

Determining Grammatical Function. In the following sentences, determine whether the italicized word is used as a *subject, predicate, direct object, indirect object, predicate noun, predicate pronoun,* or *predicate adjective.*

EXAMPLE: Chris serves a tennis *ball* with ease. _____*direct object*_____

1. Dawn hasn't read that *book* yet. _____

2. I am reading a suspenseful mystery *story*. _____

3. Please don't tell *me* the ending of the movie. _____

4. The hot *weather* has everyone on edge. _____

5. Buffalo Bill was a *rider* for the Pony Express. _____

6. Randy is too *shy* to go to the party alone. _____

7. Louis Pasteur discovered a *vaccine* for rabies. _____

8. The teacher gave *us* a quiz in geometry class this morning. _____

9. It was *she* who won the diving trophy. _____

10. The *game* of lacrosse was invented by North American Indians. _____

Identifying Phrases. Identify the italicized phrase in each of the following sentences as a *prepositional phrase, infinitive phrase, participial phrase, gerund phrase,* or *appositive phrase*.

EXAMPLE: Our television, *a portable model*, gets excellent reception. _____*appositive*_____

1. John Glenn, *a former astronaut*, is now a politician. _____

2. We were sitting *under the tree* when the lightning struck. _____

3. *Cleaning closets* is our annual spring chore. _____

4. *Having taught for twenty years*, Ms. Moss is a real pro. _____

5. Hector is helping me learn Spanish, *his native language*. _____

6. The auto mechanic will try *to diagnose the problem*. _____

7. *Working diligently on my homework* was important to me. _____

8. Dinosaurs became extinct in the *Mesozoic era*. _____

9. My friends want *to jump on the trampoline with me*. _____

10. The tree, *felled by Paul Bunyan's ax*, toppled with a crash. _____

The Simple Sentence

A **simple sentence** contains only one subject and predicate. Both the subject and predicate may be compound. *Compound* means having two or more similar parts.

> COMPOUND SUBJECT: *Luis* and *Carlos* were both in the parade.
> COMPOUND PREDICATE: Mrs. Jordan *carries mail in the daytime* and *clerks in a store in the evening.*

A compound predicate has two verbs for the same subject. At least one of the verbs has a complement.

Identifying Simple Sentences. Underline the compound parts in each of the following sentences. Tell whether these parts are *compound subjects* or *compound predicates*.

EXAMPLE: Jim and Frank play chess every noon. _compound subject_

1. The audience stood for several minutes and applauded the conductor. _____

2. Marie checked the dipstick and added more oil. _____

3. New Orleans and San Francisco are interesting cities. _____

4. The members of the cast froze in position and waited for the curtain. _____

5. Mr. Jeski washed the walls and painted the kitchen ceiling. _____

6. Sally and Frances will leave for the East on Friday. _____

7. The Siamese and the Manx are two varieties of domestic cats. _____

8. Daphne du Maurier and John Le Carré are two of my favorite modern authors. _____

9. John measured the flour and poured the milk carefully. _____

10. Georgia O'Keefe studied at several art schools and became a famous painter. _____

11. Ray and Brad were startled by the sudden clap of thunder. _____

12. Roger Bannister trained rigorously and broke the four-minute mile. _____

13. Frank went to Mr. Desmond and apologized for his behavior. _____

14. Marian and Sheila were aware of the problem. _____

15. The judge tapped her gavel and called the courtroom to order. _____

16. The unicorn and the centaur are both mythological beasts. _____

17. The porch and the patio are cooler than the house. _____

18. The fans danced in the streets and shouted from the rooftops. _____

19. Chico presided at the meeting and directed the discussion. _____

20. Julia Child writes cookbooks and has her own television show. _____

21. The Everglades and the Keys are both in Florida. _____

22. Marietta memorized the story and told it to her little nephew. _____

The Compound Sentence

The compound sentence consists of two or more simple sentences put together. The parts are joined by a comma and a coordinating conjunction (such as *and*, *yet*, *so*, *but*, *or*, *for*, *nor*), or with a semicolon. Conjunctive adverbs (*then*, *moreover*, *hence*, *consequently*, etc.) are also used to join the parts of a compound sentence. The conjunctive adverb is preceded by a semicolon. In the compound sentence, each verb has a different subject. In a simple sentence, every verb has the same subject.

We wanted to ride to town, *but* my bike had a flat tire.
Mrs. Miller likes to play tennis, *and* her niece is her favorite partner.
Steve entered the room cautiously; he had heard footsteps inside.
Our trip took five days; *consequently*, we are exhausted.

Identifying Compound and Simple Sentences. Decide which of these sentences are compound and which are simple. Place **S** or **C** in the blank after the sentence.

1. Ann signed up for woodworking, but I haven't seen her in the class. _____

2. Mr. Holmes takes his son to school, and then he goes to work. _____

3. Spiders have eight legs and are classified as arachnids. _____

4. Will you wait for me, or do you want to go ahead? _____

5. The children laughed and giggled at the puppets. _____

6. We had nearly finished our thirty-six holes of golf, and I was exhausted. _____

7. I had planned to attend the concert; however, now I can't. _____

8. The ear receives sound; it also helps us maintain a sense of balance. _____

9. Ben is afraid of the water, so he didn't want to swim. _____

10. Roland is going to audition; however, he has had little experience. _____

11. Should I carve the roast, or do you want to do it? _____

12. Irma was calm after the accident, but Ruby was very nervous. _____

13. On their vacation, the Wabshaws hiked and camped outdoors. _____

14. That farm has a windmill and generates its own electricity. _____

15. I did my grocery shopping today; consequently, our cupboard is full. _____

16. The President will hold a press conference today. _____

17. Mr. Nelson looked angry; accordingly, I wasn't eager to introduce myself. _____

18. Shall we have a picnic, or would you like to eat inside? _____

19. Dan showered and dressed in his best clothes. _____

20. The orange juice was not chilled; nevertheless, it tasted refreshing. _____

The Clause

A **clause** is a group of words containing a verb and its subject.
A clause that can stand by itself as a sentence is a **main clause**.

    _{S.}   _{V.}   _{S.}   _{V.}
He walked down the street.   Arleta plays in the band.

A clause that cannot stand by itself as a sentence is a **subordinate clause**.

    _{S.}   _{V.}
As I approached the barn (What happened?)

    _{S.} _{V.}
That flew overhead (What does the word *that* refer to?)

Phrase or Clause? A clause has a subject and a verb. A phrase does not.

    Losing my amethyst ring (phrase)   *When I lost my ring* (clause)

Identifying Clauses and Phrases. Read each sentence below. If the italicized group of words is a phrase, write **P** in the blank. If it is a clause, write **C**.

    EXAMPLE: *When I recover from the flu*, I'll leave on my trip. ___*C*___

1. *If you have solved that puzzle*, here's a harder one. _____

2. *Found only in the teeth*, enamel is the hardest substance in the body. _____

3. The box *which came in the mail today* contains Jack's new software. _____

4. Do you know *what is in the box*? _____

5. We saw the superintendent *climbing the stairs*. _____

6. *Nodding to me casually*, the principal went into her office. _____

7. *When Amy saw her father*, she rushed up to him. _____

8. The person *who was climbing the stairs* was the superintendent. _____

9. *After making several comparisons*, Greg was ready to buy a stereo. _____

10. This is the computer game *that I sent for*. _____

11. *Smiling cheerfully*, Kim walked down the hall. _____

12. *If you can spare the time*, let's go to the movie tonight. _____

13. *Striding down the hall*, Mr. Sims looked neither right nor left. _____

14. *When I came home*, I found my brother there ahead of me. _____

15. *Working at the movie studio*, Jarges learned about film editing. _____

16. *Instead of battling the cold*, the Millers went south. _____

17. *If you like Nantucket*, you will love Washington Island. _____

18. We all saw the ambulance *racing to the hospital*. _____

19. Be quiet *until the buzzer sounds*. _____

20. *Standing in the rain at the parade*, Fred got drenched. _____

The Adjective Clause

An **adjective clause** is a subordinate clause used to modify a noun or pronoun in the main clause. It may be introduced by the pronouns *who*, *whose*, *whom*, *which*, or *that*. These pronouns are called **relative pronouns** because they relate to a noun or pronoun in the sentence. Some adjective clauses begin with an introductory word such as *when* or *where*; occasionally, no introductory word is used.

> Is she the girl *whom you met at the party*? (*whom* relates to girl.)
> This is the book *that Bev read last month*. (*that* relates to *book*.)
> This is a house *where Washington slept*. (*where* is an introductory word.)
> That is the kind of dessert *I like*. (no introductory word.)

Identifying Adjective Clauses. Underline the adjective clause in each of the following sentences. Circle the word it modifies.

EXAMPLE: The (book) that he wrote has just been published.

1. Mike, whose ancestors came from Ireland, marched in the St. Patrick's Day parade.

2. The woman who lives next door is a registered nurse.

3. Williamsburg, Virginia, is a place that I'd like to visit.

4. The femurs, which are thigh bones, are the largest bones in the body.

5. There is the painting that Jason did with a palette knife.

6. Larry's letter, which he mailed Tuesday, reached me on Thursday.

7. English, which contains over six hundred thousand words, is a versatile language.

8. Phil is reading *The Call of the Wild*, which is Jack London's most famous book.

9. We live just twenty miles from O'Hare, which is the world's busiest airport.

10. Newton, Iowa, is the town where Barbara was born.

11. Jenny Lind, who was a famous soprano, was known as the Swedish Nightingale.

12. The President who established Camp David was Dwight Eisenhower.

13. This is the jacket that I would like to buy.

14. There is a chance that Norm will win the election.

15. Is this the calculator that you were using in math class yesterday?

16. Over there is the elementary school that I attended.

17. Mr. Hartmann is a history teacher who also coaches track.

18. Is that the antique show you visited on your vacation?

19. The Harveys have a dog that is fourteen years old.

20. The Appomattox Court House is the place where Lee surrendered to Grant.

The Adverb Clause

An **adverb clause** is a subordinate clause used to modify a verb, adjective, or adverb in the main clause. Every adverb clause is introduced by a subordinating conjunction. An adverb clause tells *when*, *where*, *why*, *how*, *to what extent*, or *how much* about the word it modifies.

ADVERB CLAUSES MODIFYING VERBS

We **left** the bicycle *where we had found it*. (where)
When the rain began, we **were** six miles from home. (when)
I **could** hardly **hold** my head up *because I was so sleepy*. (why)

ADVERB CLAUSES MODIFYING ADJECTIVES

Bob is **taller** *than any other boy I know*. (to what extent)
The public library is **bigger** *than it used to be*. (how much)

ADVERB CLAUSE MODIFYING AN ADVERB

Ferguson ran **faster** *than the other track stars did*. (how much)

Identifying Adverb Clauses. Underline the adverb clause in each sentence. Circle the word it modifies.

EXAMPLE: As we approached the intersection, we (saw) the Nelson's car.

1.   When I delivered the newspaper, I saw Mrs. Simpson at the window.

2.   Because that clerk was so helpful, I praised her to the store manager.

3.   The fox lay in his lair until the hunters were gone.

4.   Vince becomes nervous when he speaks in public.

5.   Please visit us whenever you are in the Wilmington area.

6.   According to legend, Nero fiddled while Rome burned.

7.   You may have trumpet lessons if you will practice an hour a day.

8.   If the jacket is too big for you, I can alter it.

9.   Children should use car safety seats until they are four years old.

10.   Phone us when you arrive in town.

11.   Marina works harder than any other member of the yearbook staff does.

12.   The movie was just beginning as George bought our tickets.

13.   When he was in his eighties, Dr. Seiler played in a string quartet.

14.   Since he joined a health club, Will has gotten more exercise.

15.   Whenever you make a promise, you must keep it!

16.   Marlene can swim better than many professional swimmers can.

17.   Although I'd never been in the Jacows' house before, I felt at home there.

18.   Before the snow began, we stacked two cords of firewood.

19.   When you listen to music on the radio, do you hum along with it?

20.   You may have the job if you will work hard at it.

Copyright © 1985 by McDougal, Littell & Company

The Noun Clause

A **noun clause** is a subordinate clause used as a noun in the sentence. A noun clause may be used as subject or direct object of the verb, as a predicate noun, as an object of the preposition, or as an appositive.

Every direct quotation preceded by words such as *She said* or *I called* is a noun clause without an introductory word.

> Mary said, "Dinner is ready." (The noun clause is the object of *said*.)
> Mary said that dinner was ready. (*that* is the introductory word.)

Identifying Noun Clauses. Underline the noun clause in each sentence. If the noun clause is the subject of the sentence, write **S** in the blank. If the noun clause is the direct object, write **D** in the blank.

EXAMPLE: I know what the answer is. ___*D*___

1. Did you know that Woody Allen's real name is Allen Konigsberg? _____

2. Lena thinks that the world needs a universal language. _____

3. Whoever phoned us didn't let the phone ring long enough. _____

4. Nutritionists say that a lack of calcium causes brittle bones. _____

5. Whether or not she should go hiking worried Julia. _____

6. Mr. Sims mentioned that he is teaching a course on wilderness survival. _____

7. That he was growing deaf was apparent to Beethoven. _____

8. Who your ancestors were makes no difference to me. _____

9. Mr. Barnes swore that he would tell the truth. _____

10. That the experiment might fail never occurred to him. _____

11. The explorers knew where the treasure was hidden. _____

12. Kyle said, "I forgot my wallet." _____

13. I knew that the safe was behind the picture. _____

14. The ancient Greeks believed that the gods lived on Mt. Olympus. _____

15. What happened on June 30, 1983, will never be forgotten in our town. _____

16. We knew that we were in for a spell of hot, humid weather. _____

17. Whoever visits us will be given a comfortable room. _____

18. Mr. Christacakos said, "School is simply a rehearsal." _____

19. We all believe that Jim will be elected class president. _____

20. Mr. Davis regrets that he didn't travel more in his youth. _____

The Complex Sentence

The complex sentence consists of one main clause and one or more subordinate clauses. The subordinate clause usually modifies a word in the main clause.

After Dan studies, he watches TV. (subordinate clause modifies *watches*)
This is the week *when the Todds leave for their vacation in the Rockies*. (subordinate clause modifies *week*)
If Ann takes the pictures, I'll develop them. (subordinate clause modifies *develop*)

Identifying Simple, Compound, and Complex Sentences. Read the following sentences. Indicate whether each sentence is *simple*, *compound*, or *complex*.

1. Caroline rang the doorbell, but no one answered it. _____

2. I wrote Anita a letter while she was away at camp. _____

3. Have you seen Mr. Shuman's garden at the back of his house? _____

4. When Marty bakes bread, he uses whole grain flour. _____

5. My sister enjoys chemistry, but she likes physics better. _____

6. After a stroke paralyzed his right arm, Leonardo Da Vinci learned to paint with his left hand. _____

7. When I'm tired, I'm not good company for anyone. _____

8. Walking slowly along the path, I saw several kinds of wildflowers. _____

9. Bananas are picked green and later turn yellow. _____

10. When the rain began, we were playing soccer. _____

11. When Uncle Jack comes to town, we all have a good time. _____

12. Mickey worked all morning, and then he relaxed in the afternoon. _____

13. Beth likes all seasons of the year, but she likes fall best. _____

14. Pearl Buck won a Nobel Prize for her novel *The Good Earth*. _____

15. Although his health was failing, Roosevelt ran for a third term. _____

16. Whistling loudly, Ken walked past the cemetery. _____

17. How many states can you see from Lookout Mountain? _____

18. If you want your car really clean, let George wash it. _____

19. I must stay home until someone comes to repair the washing machine. _____

20. Last year we saw a bluegrass festival in Connecticut, and this year we will attend the National Hollerin' Contest in North Carolina. _____

Review: Sentence and Clause

SENTENCE AND CLAUSE **127**

Identifying Simple, Compound, and Complex Sentences. Tell whether each of the following sentences is *simple*, *compound*, or *complex*.

> **EXAMPLE:** The typewriter is being overhauled. _____*simple*_____

1. Although rhubarb stalks are edible, the leaves are poisonous. _____

2. Debbie's dog helps her round up the cows and herd them to the barn. _____

3. Either it has gotten chilly out, or there is something wrong with the furnace. _____

4. We aren't allowed to watch television while we are eating. _____

5. The Wright brothers' first airplane is in the Smithsonian Institution. _____

Identifying Types of Clauses. Tell whether the italicized clause in each of the following sentences is a *noun clause*, an *adjective clause*, or an *adverb clause*.

> **EXAMPLE:** The suit *that I bought on sale* is too small. _____*adjective*_____

1. Do you know *what the formula for square roots is*? _____

2. Paul became ill *when he was in Las Vegas*. _____

3. Benjamin Franklin wrote, *"Lost time is never found again."* _____

4. *Whoever left the kitchen so messy* had better clean it up. _____

5. Once, *when Martha was very young*, she ran away from home. _____

6. Lauren, *who is our neighbor*, likes to play in our yard. _____

7. San Francisco is a city *where commuters ride cable cars*. _____

8. *What I just saw* really was hilarious. _____

9. The street looks barren *since Dutch elm disease destroyed the trees*. _____

10. *Until you are instructed otherwise*, continue with your reading. _____

Identifying Phrases and Clauses. Read each group of words below. If it is a phrase, mark **P** on the blank. If it is a clause, mark **C**.

> **EXAMPLE:** Driving down the freeway ___*P*___

1. While I was putting on my shoes _____

2. After the heavy rains _____

3. When the music stopped _____

4. Considering the amount of time _____

5. If Emma earns enough money doing odd jobs _____

Copyright © 1985 by McDougal, Littell & Company

Fragments Due to Incomplete Thoughts

A **sentence fragment** is an uncompleted sentence, one that is missing either a subject or a predicate. It is only a part, or fragment, of a sentence.

> Father at the end of the day. (Did what? Where is the verb?)
> After the movie. (What then? What is the rest of the thought?)

Correcting Fragments Resulting from Incomplete Thoughts. Read the following sentence fragments. Add the words necessary to make each into a complete sentence.

1. While hurtling through space, the astronaut _found a spaceship, pulled out his power prybar and opened the airlock_

2. At four o'clock on June 2, _I should have died, but Satan took my twin brother instead,_

3. Before the broadcast _, I died_

4. The delay in shipment _, resulted in death_

5. On a crowded subway _he died_

6. When Sam entered the cave, _he died_

7. As Susan unwrapped her gift, _she died_

8. Since Mother hurried down to the office _I will die_

9. Nothing on the grocer's shelves _but dead chickens_

10. The abandoned house in our neighborhood _is where I died._

Fragments Due to Faulty Punctuation

The first word of a sentence begins with a capital letter, and the sentence is closed by a punctuation mark: a *period*, a *question mark*, or an *exclamation mark*. When the writer inserts a period and capital letter too soon, the result is called a **period fault**.

FRAGMENT: While she was reading. She fell asleep.
SENTENCE: While she was reading, she fell asleep.
FRAGMENT: The Senators stood up. When the President entered the room.
SENTENCE: The Senators stood up when the President entered the room.

Correcting Fragments Resulting from Incorrect Punctuation. Find the fragments in each of the following groups of words. Correctly rewrite each by either changing the punctuation or adding the words needed to make a complete sentence.

1. After we went to the movie. We discussed it for hours. _____

   _____

2. The invention of electricity. Made gas lights obsolete. _____

   _____

3. Since we had eaten such a big lunch. A light supper. _____

   _____

4. Because television requires no feedback. Viewers become passive. _____

   _____

5. After our car was washed. It looked much better. _____

   _____

6. Our team has won the conference title. Twice in the last three years. _____

   _____

7. Although Dad works hard. He always takes time to relax. _____

   _____

8. Crossing the street with two bags of groceries. I stumbled and fell. _____

   _____

9. After Stefan returned from his canoe trip. He sold his canoe. _____

   _____

10. Unless you are sure of the answer. A blank space on your paper. _____

   _____

Phrases as Fragments

A phrase does not contain both a verb and a subject. Therefore, it is not a complete sentence. A prepositional phrase is usually easy to spot.

FRAGMENT: A brand new station wagon stands. In their driveway.
SENTENCE: A brand new station wagon stands in their driveway.

A verbal phrase may be harder to spot as a fragment, especially if it contains a verbal that ends in *-ing*. No word ending in *-ing* can be a complete verb unless it is a one-syllable word such as *sing*, *ring*, or *bring*. If an *-ing* word is preceded by *is*, *are*, or some other form of *be*, the two words together are a verb.

PARTICIPLE: looking, running   **COMPLETE VERB:** is looking, was running

A long infinitive phrase may seem like a sentence, but it does not have a subject.

INCORRECT: The dog is at the vet's. To be washed and trimmed.
CORRECT: The dog is at the vet's to be washed and trimmed.

An appositive phrase may seem like a sentence, but it always lacks a verb.

FRAGMENT: Her new calculator, an unusual model.
SENTENCE: Her new calculator, an unusual model, *is* the size of a credit card.

Completing Fragments. Rewrite each group of words to form a complete sentence.

1. He is Running down the street. _____

_____

2. I know the best thing to do. we have To present our case before the Governor. _____

_____

3. The knights wore armor. To protect themselves in battle. _____

_____

4. Sally boards her horse. At a neighbor's barn. _____

_____

5. The movie, a science fiction thriller, was dead _____

_____

6. John, cutting the grass in the front yard, died _____

_____

7. Reading quietly, Mother didn't hear us come in. _____

_____

8. That book on how to grow plants indoors, was dead. _____

_____

Clauses as Fragments

A subordinate clause cannot stand alone as a sentence. A sentence may be changed into a subordinate clause by having a subordinating conjunction placed before it.

SENTENCE: The dentist began drilling.
SUBORDINATE CLAUSE: Until the dentist began drilling . . .

Writers sometimes mistakenly treat a subordinate clause as though it were a sentence.

INCORRECT: John was late. Because he couldn't find his keys.
CORRECT: John was late because he couldn't find his keys.

Eliminating Fragments. Rewrite each of the following to form complete sentences.

EXAMPLE: While hurrying across the street. Mrs. Olson stumbled. _____ *While hurrying across the street, Mrs. Olson stumbled.* _____

1. While the patient lay on the operating table, *he died* _____

2. I'm exhausted. Because I've been walking for three hours. _____

3. My father *died* After he drove home in a new car. _____

4. Since Sylvia has a new job, *she will die* _____

5. Before we move south, *we will die* _____

6. Julie was elected class president. Although she's new in school. _____

7. When Andrew looked at the computer. _____

8. After our English class read the folk tale. _____

9. Unless you would rather wait till spring. _____

10. The audience applauded. When the astronaut finished her address. _____

A **run-on sentence** is two or more sentences written as though they were one sentence. Run-on sentences occur when the writer has failed to use an end mark, such as a period, at the end of each sentence.

    RUN-ON: Bill broke his arm it has given him a lot of trouble.
    CORRECT: Bill broke his arm. It has given him a lot of trouble.

Most run-on sentences are the result of a **comma fault**. A comma is used to join two or more sentences when each sentence should really stand alone.

    COMMA FAULT: There was a frost last night, it killed most of the flowers.
    CORRECT: There was a frost last night. It killed most of the flowers.

How To Avoid the Run-on Sentence. If two or more subjects are closely related, it is often a good idea to combine them into one sentence. There are three ways to join sentences correctly:

1. Use a comma and a coordinating conjunction:

   This summer I can work at the hardware store, or I can be a lifeguard.

2. Use a semicolon:

   Lanolin comes from wool; it is used in many ointments and cosmetics.

3. Use a semicolon and a conjunctive adverb:

   We ate a big lunch; nevertheless, we were hungry again by six o'clock.

Correcting Run-on Sentences. Put the necessary punctuation in these sentences.

    EXAMPLE: Mark took chemistry this year, he'll take physics next year.

1. The Pilgrims landed in the winter, it was too late to plant crops.

2. We won't go on vacation till August we're ready to go right now!

3. Come over to our house, we'd like to see you.

4. Orange drinks taste like orange juice, nevertheless, they are not as nutritious.

5. It's been a cold spring, hence, we've been slow in putting in our garden.

6. We saw the exhibit at the art gallery then we stopped at Nancy's house.

7. Succotash is an American Indian dish it is made from corn and lima beans.

8. Jupiter has twelve moons, it is the largest planet in the solar system.

9. I like Langston Hughes's poetry I also love his stories.

10. The Millers live on Elm Street, they've lived there twelve years.

11. Ralph studies hard he's trying to win a scholarship for next year.

12. Robert Frost was born in California, however, he is considered a New England poet.

13. We spent a month in Salem last year, consequently, we got to know the city.

14. Vanessa has studied dance for four years, furthermore, she's had two years of gymnastic training.

Run-on Sentences (II)

Correcting Run-on Sentences. Put the necessary punctuation in these sentences.

EXAMPLE: Our dog is lost; he's been gone for two days.

1. I looked up *endocrinology* in the dictionary, then I looked it up in the encyclopedia.

2. You tell me your ambition, then I'll tell you mine.

3. Don writes short stories and poems, furthermore, he keeps a daily journal.

4. You cook the dinner I'll do the dishes.

5. A cricket does not have ears instead, it has membranes on its legs that respond to sound waves.

6. Lila has a beautiful voice she'll sing a solo in the holiday concert.

7. My uncle has an unusual job he writes greeting cards.

8. Our dentist likes to play softball he joined an amateur league last year.

9. I'd like to go to Italy, all my ancestors came from there.

10. The impala is a graceful African antelope it can leap effortlessly as far as thirty feet.

11. People always remember my birthday it's April Fool's Day!

12. The Sewells would like to tour the South this summer, however, they don't have enough vacation time.

13. This year Winston is working at an art supply shop, last year he worked at a grocery.

14. The lecturer knew a great deal about psychology, however, his speech was above the heads of most of his audience.

15. The Pennsylvania Dutch are not really Dutch they are German.

16. Ms. Owens has read most of the books in our public library, furthermore, she has over three hundred books of her own.

17. Miss Tilden knows hundreds of people by name nevertheless, she has few real friends or close associates.

18. The marlin leapt from the water, then it plunged out of sight.

19. We had quite a storm last night, there was lots of thunder and lightning.

20. In high school forty years ago Mr. Stillwell learned to type, that knowledge has always been useful to him.

21. Erik occasionally tells us stories about the years he lived in Sweden, I think he would like to return there someday.

22. The southern part of the state has had heavy rains and severe flooding for three days, consequently the President has declared eight counties a federal disaster area.

23. Many people fish with a few pieces of simple equipment however, serious anglers use a whole array of rods, reels, and lures.

24. Nasturtiums are easy to grow they actually prefer poor soil and they require almost no care.

Distinguishing Fragments from Complete Sentences. Read each group of words below carefully. All are punctuated as sentences, but some are really fragments. After each fragment, write an **F** on the blank. After each sentence, write an **S** on the blank.

> **EXAMPLE:**   Thinking he was finished with his work.   *F*

1. The people who settled the Midwest. _____

2. Directly overhead, a helicopter hovered. _____

3. Climbing into bed and falling asleep. _____

4. Someone is calling for help. _____

5. Were from another planet. _____

Rewriting Sentences. All the items below need revision. Some are fragments and need to be rewritten as complete sentences. Others are run-ons and need to be rewritten as two sentences or punctuated properly as one sentence.

> **EXAMPLE:**   I spilled something on my shirt. While eating breakfast.
> *While eating my breakfast, I spilled something on my shirt.*

1. Arthur easily pulled the sword out of the stone, he was the true king. _____

_____

2. Forgetting all about his appointment. Mr. Marist took the afternoon off. _____

_____

3. If you could travel anywhere you wanted. _____

_____

4. My grandmother left me an inheritance, I can't use it until I'm twenty-one. _____

_____

5. Sometimes, when I am in a very good mood. _____

_____

6. Today is my birthday I'm now sixteen. _____

_____

7. Even though Audrey had never ridden a horse. _____

_____

8. We looked everywhere for the keys. Even under the furniture. _____

_____

The Past Forms of Verbs (I)

A **regular verb** is one that forms its past and past participle by adding *-ed* or *-d* to the present form of the verb. Most verbs in English fall into this category.

PRESENT	PAST	PAST PARTICIPLE
walk	walked	(have) walked
dance	danced	(have) danced

An **irregular verb** is one that does not form its past and past participle by adding *-ed* or *-d* to the present form. Approximately sixty commonly used verbs fall into this category.

One group of irregular verbs has the same form for the present, the past, and the past participle.

PRESENT	PAST	PAST PARTICIPLE
burst	burst	(have) burst
cost	cost	(have) cost
hit	hit	(have) hit
shut	shut	(have) shut

A second group of irregular verbs has the same form for both the past and the past participle.

PRESENT	PAST	PAST PARTICIPLE
bring	brought	(have) brought
fight	fought	(have) fought
fling	flung	(have) flung
get	got	(have) got or gotten
lend	lent	(have) lent

The past tense form is used alone. The past participle is used with forms of *be* or *have*.

Using Verbs Correctly. In each of the following sentences, the present form of a verb is given in parentheses. Substitute either the past or the past participle, whichever the sentence requires.

EXAMPLE: She (fight) for her right to speak. _____ *fought* _____

1. I (lend) Ken a book three weeks ago. _____

2. The Spanish (bring) the first horses to America. _____

3. I have (hit) many home runs in the past. _____

4. Ms. Lindel has (dance) with the Civic Ballet for two years. _____

5. The zookeeper has (fling) a net over the rampaging tiger. _____

6. Before she left, Marta (shut) the doors of the supply cabinet. _____

7. The new bridge has (cost) the city a great deal of money. _____

8. The principal informed us that the water pipes had (burst). _____

9. Last night we (walk) down to the beach. _____

10. We (get) some commemorative stamps at the post office. _____

The Past Forms of Verbs (II)

Another group of irregular verbs adds -n or -en to the past form to make the past participle.

PRESENT	PAST	PAST PARTICIPLE
bear	bore	(have) borne
bite	bit	(have) bitten
choose	chose	(have) chosen
freeze	froze	(have) frozen
wear	wore	(have) worn

Still another group of irregular verbs changes the middle vowel from *i* in the present, to *a* in the past, and to *u* in the past participle.

PRESENT	PAST	PAST PARTICIPLE
begin	began	(have) begun
drink	drank	(have) drunk
sing	sang	(have) sung
spring	sprang *or* sprung	(have) sprung
swim	swam	(have) swum

Using Verbs Correctly. In each of the following sentences, the present form of a verb is given in parentheses. Substitute either the past or the past participle, whichever the sentence requires.

EXAMPLE: Rene has (swim) in every competition this year. _____ *swum*

1. President Lincoln (bear) his troubles bravely. _____

2. Mario has (sing) in several high school musicals. _____

3. Anna hasn't (begin) to think about her choice of college yet. _____

4. As John Smith was about to die, Pocahontas (spring) to his rescue. _____

5. Paul (bite) into the granola bar greedily. _____

6. I have (freeze) the blueberries we picked yesterday. _____

7. Traditionally, the villagers have (wear) elaborate costumes. _____

8. Which show have you (choose) to win the Academy Award? _____

9. This morning at breakfast, Barbara (drink) a glass of milk. _____

10. The trapdoor (spring) open and the magician disappeared. _____

11. I (wear) braces for three years. _____

12. Henry Luce (begin) publishing *Time* magazine in 1923. _____

13. Americans have (drink) carbonated beverages since 1807. _____

14. Our tiny rowboat had (spring) a leak. _____

15. Sheena Easton (sing) at the concert last month. _____

The Past Forms of Verbs (III)

Another group of irregular verbs makes the past participle from the present form.

PRESENT	PAST	PAST PARTICIPLE
come	came	(have) come
do	did	(have) done
draw	drew	(have) drawn
fall	fell	(have) fallen
grow	grew	(have) grown
know	knew	(have) known
run	ran	(have) run
see	saw	(have) seen
take	took	(have) taken
throw	threw	(have) thrown
write	wrote	(have) written

Using Verbs Correctly. In each of these sentences, the present form of a verb is given. Substitute either the past or the past participle, whichever the sentence requires.

EXAMPLE: Sandi (do) the sound effects for the variety show last year. _____*did*_____

1. Sherlock Holmes had (draw) his conclusions based on careful observation. _____

2. I'm afraid that your car has (run) out of gas. _____

3. Have you (take) out the garbage yet? _____

4. A city worker (come) to inspect the restaurant. _____

5. The interviewer asked about the work I have (do) in the past. _____

6. Last night the campers (see) a black bear and two deer. _____

7. One horse (throw) its rider during the parade. _____

8. *The Pearl* was one of the best novels that John Steinbeck ever (write). _____

9. I have never (know) a more patient person than Michelle. _____

10. That oak tree has (grow) to an enormous height. _____

11. Icarus (fall) to earth when the sun melted the wax of his wings. _____

12. During his vacation last summer, Stan (take) over fifty pictures. _____

13. In art class last year, we (draw) pictures of ourselves. _____

14. Gwen had never (see) flamenco dancing before. _____

15. Judy Blume has (write) many interesting and insightful books. _____

16. The time has (come) to send a new quarterback into the game. _____

17. Albert (grow) up to be a world-famous scientist. _____

18. One of the children had (fall) from the swing. _____

Progressive and Emphatic Verbs

To show ongoing action, you use the **progressive forms** of the verb. Progressive forms are made by using the forms of *be* with the present participle.

is singing	has been asking
was studying	must be working
will be painting	might have been ringing

To give special emphasis to a statement, you use the **emphatic forms** of the verb. Emphatic forms are made by using *do*, *does*, or *did* with the present form of the verb.

I *do like* your haircut.   I *did enjoy* the movie.

Recognizing Progressive and Emphatic Verb Forms. Tell whether the italicized verb in each sentence is progressive or emphatic.

EXAMPLE: I *have been answering* the phone all morning. _____ *progressive*

1. Pinchas Zukerman *was playing* the violin. _____

2. The mayor *did listen* to our complaints after all. _____

3. The students *were using* tempera paints and narrow, flat brushes. _____

4. I *do want* to help around the house. _____

5. In Japan, people *have been eating* tofu for centuries. _____

6. Mariana *was assembling* a model of the space shuttle. _____

7. Valarie *does try* to eat sensibly. _____

8. "I *did follow* the directions on the bottle," said the patient. _____

9. Sam *does work* very hard indeed. _____

10. The President's secretary *will be sending* you an invitation. _____

11. Jack *must have been sleeping* when you called. _____

12. Bill really *did find* the wallet on the sidewalk. _____

13. Alpha Centauri *does shine* more brightly than many other stars. _____

14. Vanessa *has been planning* a trip to San Antonio. _____

15. Children *do have* only twenty teeth, while adults have thirty-two. _____

16. Luckily, I *did have* the receipt for the merchandise. _____

17. Government officials *are looking* for solutions to the problem. _____

18. Mr. Jarvis *is writing* a book about wildlife preserves in Kenya. _____

19. Poet Anne Sexton *did win* the Pulitzer Prize in 1967. _____

20. Carlos and I *shall be building* the set for the fall play. _____

Verb Tense

Most verbs change their forms to show present, past, and future time. Another word for the time to which a verb refers is **tense**. In English, there are three simple tenses and three perfect tenses:

	SIMPLE	PERFECT
PRESENT	need	have needed
PAST	needed	had needed
FUTURE	shall (will) need	shall (will) have needed

Each of these verb tenses also has a **progressive form** that is made by combining a form of *be* with the present participle.

	SIMPLE	PERFECT
PRESENT PROGRESSIVE	am (is, are) needing	has (have) been needing
PAST PROGRESSIVE	was (were) needing	had been needing
FUTURE PROGRESSIVE	shall (will) be needing	shall (will) have been needing

Identifying Verb Tense. Write the tense of the italicized verb in each sentence. The tense may be *present*, *past*, *future*, *present perfect*, *past perfect*, or *future perfect*.

EXAMPLE: Juanita *will study* this summer in Mexico City. _____*future*_____

1. The students *have tried* to keep the cafeteria clean. _____

2. Sun Lee *shall* always *remember* her trip to the United States. _____

3. Mistletoe *grows* in the branches of trees. _____

4. Edmund Halley correctly *predicted* the return of Halley's comet. _____

5. Only Don Larsen *has pitched* a perfect game in the World Series. _____

6. I *had thought* that bald eagles are bald, but they are not. _____

Identifying Progressive Forms. Identify the italicized verbs in the following sentences as *present progressive*, *past progressive*, *future progressive*, *present perfect progressive*, *past perfect progressive*, or *future perfect progressive*.

EXAMPLE: The puppies *had been playing* in the closet. *past perfect progressive*

1. The mosquitoes *were bothering* me all evening. _____

2. The crowd *has been cheering* throughout the game. _____

3. People *have been observing* the stars for thousands of years. _____

4. José *is thinking* about possible careers. _____

5. At noon, David *will have been sleeping* for thirteen hours. _____

6. The cat *had been studying* the aquarium. _____

Voice and Mood

The Active and Passive Voice. When the subject performs the action expressed by the verb, the verb is in the active voice. When the subject receives the action of the verb, the verb is in the passive voice.

ACTIVE: Dan cooked breakfast.   PASSIVE: Breakfast was cooked by Dan.

Mood. The mood of a verb shows the speaker or writer's attitude.

The **indicative mood**, which we use most of the time, shows that we are talking or writing about something that has happened, is happening, or definitely will happen.

The **imperative mood** is used to express a command or a request and has only one tense—the present—and one person—the second.

The **subjunctive mood** is used to express wishes, commands, and conditions that are doubtful or contrary to fact. It is also used to express commands or requests after *that*. The forms for subjunctive and indicative verbs are identical, with these exceptions:

1. The *s* is omitted from the verb in the third-person singular.
2. The present tense of the verb *to be* is always *be*.
3. The past tense of the verb *to be* is always *were*.

Using the Active Voice. The following sentences are written in the passive voice. Rewrite each sentence in the active voice.

1.   The meal was prepared by Julia Child. _____

_____

2.   Fruit crops in Florida were destroyed by the cold weather. _____

_____

3.   The game was won by the Denver Broncos. _____

_____

4.   A speech was delivered by the secretary of the Student Council. _____

_____

5.   A mouse was cornered by the cat. _____

_____

Identifying Mood. Tell the mood of each italicized verb.

1.   If I *were* you, I would write a letter to the editor. _____

2.   *Send* me a postcard from Seattle. _____

3.   The teacher asked that Marty *complete* the paper tonight. _____

4.   In May of 1983, a severe earthquake *occurred* in Japan. _____

5.   *Carry* the canoe down to the lake. _____

Commonly Confused Verbs

Lie and Lay. The verb *lie* has eight or nine meanings, all having the idea of "being in a horizontal position" or "remaining or being situated in a particular place or condition." The verb *lay* means "to place or to put." These two verbs have the following principal parts:

PRESENT	PAST	PAST PARTICIPLE
lie	lay	(have) lain
lay	laid	(have) laid

Sit and Set. The verb *sit* usually means "to rest with the legs bent and the back upright," but there are many other related meanings. The verb *set* means "to place or to put."

PRESENT	PAST	PAST PARTICIPLE
sit	sat	(have) sat
set	set	(have) set

Rise and Raise. The verb *rise* means "to go to a higher position." The verb *raise* means "to lift to a higher position."

PRESENT	PAST	PAST PARTICIPLE
rise	rose	(have) risen
raise	raised	(have) raised

The verbs *lie*, *sit*, and *rise* are intransitive. They do not have objects. The verbs *lay*, *set*, and *raise* are transitive. They almost always do have objects.

Using Verbs Correctly. In the following sentences, underline the correct verb.

EXAMPLE: Mrs. Norman (lay, laid) down for a nap.

1. Please (sit, set) the plate on the table.

2. Last fall we (sat, set) the jack-o'-lantern on the front porch.

3. The jeweler had (sat, set) the stone incorrectly.

4. The king then (rose, raised) to address his subjects.

5. Please (lie, lay) the cloth on the table.

6. Our dog never (lies, lays) down when told to do so.

7. The official had already (risen, raised) the flag to start the race.

8. The President was pleased that prices had not (risen, raised) during August.

9. Did Marsha (sit, set) aside enough time to finish her homework?

10. Phillip had never (sat, set) in an airplane before.

11. Mom and Dad have already (lain, laid) the tile in the kitchen.

12. Those papers have (lain, laid) on his desk for several days now.

13. The Romans (lay, laid) roads throughout their empire.

14. Lisa del Gioconda (sat, set) for the painting known as the "Mona Lisa."

15. Do you think that PSAT scores will (rise, raise) again at our school?

16. Ms. Corso (rose, raised) her voice above the commotion in the room.

Copyright © 1985 by McDougal, Littell & Company

Review: Verb Usage

Using Verbs Correctly. Circle the correct verb in each of the following sentences.

1. Who first (brought, brung) parakeets to North America?

2. The children have (drank, drunk) most of the orange juice.

3. That muskrat has (swum, swam) across the lake several times.

4. Alberto has (ran, run) in several marathons.

5. Marlene had (laid, lain) her coat over the back of a chair.

6. Because of the heat in the car, the birthday balloons all (burst, bursted).

Using Various Forms of Verbs. Rewrite the following sentences, changing the verb to the form shown in parentheses.

1. Adrienne enjoyed the sequel to the film. (emphatic) _____

_____

2. My family and I lived in Dallas at the time. (past progressive) _____

_____

3. I opened a savings account of my own. (present perfect) _____

_____

4. The sports commentators predict a very close pennant race. (present perfect

progressive) _____

_____

5. The debate between the Student Council candidates was moderated by Malcolm and

Marsha. (active voice) _____

_____

Using the Indicative, Imperative, and Subjunctive Moods. Write sentences using the verbs given in parentheses.

1. (indicative form of the verb *laugh*) _____

_____

2. (imperative form of the verb *write*) _____

_____

3. (subjunctive form of the verb *be*) _____

_____

Agreement in Number (I)

There are two numbers in grammar: **singular** and **plural**. A word is singular in number if it refers to one person or thing. A word is plural if it refers to more than one person or thing.

Except for *be*, English verbs show a difference between singular and plural only in the third person and only in the present tense. The third person singular present form ends in *s*.

I, you, we, they *talk*   he, she, it *talks*

The second person pronoun *you* is always used with the plural form of the verb: *you are*, *you were*. The difference between singular and plural forms of *be* is shown in the past tense as well as the present tense.

Present Tense		Past Tense	
SINGULAR	**PLURAL**	**SINGULAR**	**PLURAL**
I *am*	we *are*	I *was*	we *were*
you *are*	you *are*	you *were*	you *were*
he, she, it *is*	they *are*	he, she, it *was*	they *were*

Choosing the Correct Verb Form. Underline the correct form of the verb in each sentence below.

1. (Was, Were) you at the meeting last night?

2. We (was, were) discussing this year's Heisman trophy winner.

3. (Is, Are) *Little Women* your sister's favorite book?

4. As the dentist (was, were) drilling, I tried to think of pleasant things.

5. (Is, Are) your team ahead of mine in the conference?

6. Sarah (commutes, commute) to her job in the city.

7. (Was, Were) you playing tennis with Joe last night?

8. The first human heart transplant (was, were) performed in 1967.

9. Where (was, were) they going when we saw them last night?

10. How fast (was, were) the rocket going at lift-off?

11. (Wasn't, Weren't) the twins good in the play?

12. The Jeraks (is, are) going to Vermont next week.

13. They (was, were) not amused by the comedian.

14. They (was, were) out of town when the house burned.

15. (Has, Have) the Maxeys found a new apartment?

16. The Millers (was, were) happy about the outcome of the election.

17. You (was, were) up early this morning.

18. How (does, do) Art manage to do so much in one day?

19. (Was, Were) you at the speech meet last Saturday?

20. The Beatles (was, were) from Liverpool, England.

The verb agrees only with its subject. Occasionally, a word with a different number than the subject occurs between the subject and the verb. This word or group of words does not change the number of the verb even though it is closer to the verb than the subject is.

> One of the twins is taller than his brother.
> The ball thrown by the boys has gone through the Browns' window. (*ball* is the subject of *has gone*.)

The words *with*, *together with*, *along with*, and *as well as* are prepositions. The objects of these prepositions have no effect upon the number of the verb.

> The captain, together with the crew members, has mapped the coastline of the island. (*captain* is the subject of *has mapped*.)
> My aunt, along with my cousins, is visiting us. (*aunt* is the subject of *is visiting*.)

Choosing the Correct Verb Form. Underline the correct form of the verb in each sentence below.

1. The members of the marching band (has, have) arrived for practice.

2. The price of school lunches (keeps, keep) increasing every year.

3. The students, along with their art teacher (is, are) going to the exhibit of African art.

4. One of the women (is, are) planning to give a karate demonstration.

5. (Has, Have) the pair of earrings been found?

6. A sale of cassette tapes (has, have) been scheduled for next Monday.

7. Mother Goose, famous in nursery rhymes, (is, are) buried in Boston.

8. The volunteers at the hospital (is, are) meeting at ten o'clock.

9. The trees, as well as the garden, (is, are) being destroyed by insects.

10. The library, with its thousands of books, (is, are) open to all.

11. Ms. Taylor, along with the other tourists, (is, are) waiting to kiss the Blarney stone.

12. The lead singer, together with the other musicians, (is, are) now leaving the stage for a break before the second part of the show.

13. Several citizens of Salem (was, were) opposed to the witch trials.

14. Janine, along with her friends, (is, are) planning to be in Washington next week.

15. Ms. Thomas, together with other members of the club, (is, are) planning a golf tournament for the spring.

16. One of America's major achievements (was, were) the moon landing.

17. Announcement of the winner (is, are) being made today.

18. The crossword puzzle, found in most newspapers, (was, were) invented in 1913.

19. The set of socket wrenches (is, are) not in the garage.

20. Paavo Nurmi, who held twenty world running records, (was, were) known everywhere as "The Flying Finn."

Indefinite Pronouns

Some indefinite pronouns are always singular. Others are always plural. *Some*, *none*, *all*, *any*, and *most* are singular when they refer to a portion or a quantity. They are plural when they refer to a number of individual items.

SINGULAR			PLURAL	SINGULAR OR PLURAL	
each	someone	nobody	several	some	any
either	everyone	somebody	few	none	most
neither	anyone	everybody	both	all	
one	no one		many		

One the books *was* lost.
Several in the club *are* good at speaking in public.
Some of the money *was* missing.
Some of the windows *are* dirty.

Choosing the Correct Verb Form. Underline the correct verb.

EXAMPLE: Somebody (<u>is</u>, are) at the door.

1.   Most of the library books (has, have) been returned.

2.   Everybody on the bus (was, were) going to Cleveland or Cincinnati.

3.   Few of the students (is, are) going to play in the chess tournament.

4.   Neither of the two Senators (has, have) explained the matter.

5.   All of us (is, are) hoping that Steve will set a record for high jumping.

6.   Nobody (knows, know) the answer to your question.

7.   Several of the Jacksons (is, are) excellent singers.

8.   One of King Arthur's knights (was, were) Sir Lancelot.

9.   Everyone at the birthday party (was, were) somehow related to Jean.

10.   No one (is, are) here to help me put up the decorations.

11.   (Is, Are) there any of the bran muffins left?

12.   Both of Bill's sisters (is, are) going to Ohio State next fall.

13.   Many of the club members (wants, want) to visit Disneyland.

14.   (Is, Are) somebody looking for a book by James Thurber?

15.   Some of the salad (has, have) been eaten already.

16.   Many of the world's nations (has, have) banned whale hunting.

17.   The dairy farmer was happy that none of the milk (was, were) sour.

18.   Each of us (was, were) planning a trip during spring break.

19.   (Has, Have) anyone here ever ridden the swanboats in the Boston Public Garden?

20.   Several of these retired people (has, have) begun working as volunteer tutors.

21.   I didn't realize that each of the presents (was, were) mailed separately.

22.   Most of our lawn chairs (is, are) rather uncomfortable.

Compound Subjects

Compound subjects joined by *and* are plural.

Illusion and prestidigitation *are* types of magic tricks.

Singular words joined by *or*, *nor*, *either-or*, *neither-nor* are singular.

Neither Barbara nor Miguel *is* in the Spanish club.
Was either roast beef or baked ham on the menu?

When a singular word and plural word are joined by *or* or *nor*, the verb agrees with the subject nearer to it.

Neither Ann nor her friends *are* coming to the block party.
Either the veterinarian or her assistants *give* the shots.

Choosing the Correct Verb Form with Compound Subjects. In each of the following sentences, underline the correct form of the verb.

EXAMPLE: Alice and Mary (plans, <u>plan</u>) to attend the same college.

1. Neither the coach nor the players (was, were) satisfied with the umpire's decision.

2. Alicia or her mother (is, are) going to collect for the Red Cross this week.

3. Glen and Amy (hopes, hope) to become journalists.

4. The author's first two novels and last short story (is, are) often quoted.

5. Either the Amazon or the Nile (is, are) the world's longest river.

6. Neither movies nor television (appeals, appeal) to me very much.

7. Softball and football (is, are) John's favorite sports.

8. Either a Jersey or a Guernsey (is, are) a good choice for a dairy cow.

9. San Diego and Santa Fé (is, are) two of my favorite western cities.

10. Neither the principal nor the dean (is, are) here today.

11. Andrew Wyeth and other painters (has, have) had exhibits in the museum.

12. Chinese and English (is, are) spoken by more people than any other languages.

13. Neither Tom nor José (remembers, remember) the combination for the lock.

14. Either Agatha Christie or John Le Carré (is, are) Coretta's favorite writer.

15. Neither Ms. Washington nor the other lawyers (is, are) willing to take the case.

16. The debaters and their coach (is, are) awaiting the decision.

17. Neither the crew members nor the cargo (has, have) been recovered.

18. Ramon's cap and gloves (has, have) been found.

19. Neither the President nor his aides (plans, plan) to visit the disaster site.

20. Either George or Bill (deliver, delivers) the newspapers every morning.

21. Neither the marine biologist nor the fishermen (was, were) quarantined.

22. The weavers and the designer (is, are) working on the project together.

When the subject follows the verb, you must think ahead to the subject to decide whether the verb is to be singular or plural.

This problem arises in sentences beginning with contractions made from *There* and *Here*. It also arises in questions beginning with *Who*, *Why*, *Where*, *What*, and *How*.

INCORRECT: Here's the records.
CORRECT: Here *are* the records.
INCORRECT: There's my brothers now.
CORRECT: There *are* my brothers now.
INCORRECT: Who's the women at the window?
CORRECT: Who *are* the women at the window?
INCORRECT: What's the solutions?
CORRECT: What *are* the solutions?

Choosing the Correct Verb Form. Underline the correct form of the verb.

EXAMPLE: (What's, <u>What are</u>) the problems?

1. (Here's, Here are) the acrylic paints you ordered for your art project.

2. (Who's, Who are) Earl's helpers on the lighting crew?

3. (What's, What are) your suggestions for cleaning up the alley?

4. On the Acropolis (was, were) the Parthenon and the Temple of Nike.

5. (There's, There are) several good reasons for learning another language.

6. (Here's, Here are) the running shoes Maureen wants to buy.

7. (How's, How are) all your tropical fish?

8. (Why's, Why are) all the shops in Paris closed in August?

9. (There's, There are) jets and gliders in the air show.

10. (Who's, Who are) the contestants in the floor exercise competition?

11. Near the two-lane highway (was, were) an old house and a barn.

12. Behind the counter (stands, stand) the service manager and her assistant.

13. (What's, What are) the jokes you were going to tell me?

14. (Why's, Why are) folk ballads usually so sad?

15. (Here's, Here are) the fried chicken and salad Louise ordered.

16. In front of us (was, were) Meryl Streep and her child.

17. (Here's, Here are) the muddy shoes you left on the patio.

18. Outside the door (sits, sit) three pots of chrysanthemums.

19. (What's What are) your reasons for making that statement?

20. (What's What are) the two tallest buildings in the United States?

21. (Why's, Why are) there three pairs of boots in the hallway?

22. (Here's, Here are) the best news you've heard all day!

Using *Don't* and *Doesn't*

The word *does* and the contraction *doesn't* are used with singular nouns and with the pronouns *he*, *she*, and *it*. The word *do* and the contraction *don't* are used with plural nouns and with the pronouns *I*, *we*, *you*, and *they*.

DOES, DOESN'T	DO, DON'T
our friend does	our friends do
he doesn't	we don't
she doesn't	you don't
it doesn't	they don't

Using *Does* and *Don't* Correctly. Underline the correct word in each sentence below.

1. Amy (doesn't, don't) like to read more than one book at a time.

2. The airplane (doesn't, don't) have any seats in the non-smoking section.

3. Why (doesn't, don't) Peggy want to do a report on quasars?

4. The rug (doesn't, don't) cover all the floor.

5. Our dog (doesn't, don't) remember the tricks that we taught him.

6. (Doesn't, Don't) an African elephant weigh about 14,000 pounds?

7. Ms. Ogden likes to play golf, but Mr. Ogden (doesn't, don't).

8. Water (doesn't, don't) boil until it reaches 212° Fahrenheit.

9. Why (doesn't, don't) the moon shine in the daytime?

10. The menu (doesn't, don't) include baked ham.

11. The boy in the red shirt and blue jeans (doesn't, don't) know where the cafeteria is.

12. Zucchini, lettuce, and cucumbers (doesn't, don't) contain many calories.

13. The photograph of Princess Diana (doesn't, don't) even look like her.

14. That vending machine (doesn't, don't) even give correct change.

15. Our debate with the Thornwood team (doesn't, don't) begin till ten o'clock.

16. The President and his cabinet members (doesn't, don't) meet until tomorrow.

17. Why (doesn't, don't) Dan ring the bell instead of knocking?

18. The director, along with the members of the band, (doesn't, don't) report for rehearsals until tomorrow.

19. The potato salad (doesn't, don't) taste good; we'd better throw it out.

20. (Doesn't, Don't) the Platte River flow through Nebraska and Missouri?

21. (Doesn't, Don't) the uniforms have to be drycleaned first?

22. I will be disappointed if the tape recorder (don't, doesn't) work again.

23. (Doesn't, Don't) he want to enter the kayak race?

24. The cabins in the state park (doesn't, don't) have electricity.

25. (Doesn't, Don't) the village board make the final decision about the festival?

Collective Nouns. A collective noun names a group of people or things; *band*, *jury*, *crew*, *group*, *team*. When a writer refers to a group acting together as one unit, the collective noun is used with a singular verb. When the writer refers to the individuals in the group acting separately, the collective noun is used with a plural verb.

> Our band *is* the best in the country. (united action)
> Our band *were* wearing their new uniforms. (separate actions)

Nouns Plural in Form. Some nouns are plural in form but are singular in meaning: *news*, *mumps*, *measles*. There are many words ending in *-ics* that may be singular or plural: *politics*, *athletics*, *economics*. These words are singular when used to refer to a school subject or general practice.

> Athletics is one way to get a scholarship. (singular)
> His favorite athletics are track and golf. (plural)

Choosing the Correct Verb Form. Underline the correct form of the verb in each sentence below.

> EXAMPLE: The news of the day (is, are) the subject of Mrs. Martin's commentary.

1. The team (was, were) all grinning after their victory.

2. The jury (has, have) reached a verdict.

3. Measles (has, have) been on the decline since the vaccine was developed.

4. The community theater company (was, were) started in 1981 and immediately achieved enormous success.

5. (Is, Are) mumps more serious in older patients?

6. Economics (is, are) being taught in the senior classes.

7. The audience (is, are) taking their seats now.

8. Our class (is, are) posing for their yearbook pictures today.

9. Civics (is, are) a study of the rights and duties of citizens.

10. The senator's politics (is, are) sometimes questioned by his constituents.

11. The Student Affairs Committee (reports, report) directly to the principal.

12. The news on the front page (was, were) all good today.

13. The contents of the briefcase (was, were) a notebook and a chess set.

14. All the members of my family (is, are) interested in athletics.

15. The newspaper reporter's ethics (was, were) seriously questioned during the trial.

16. The couple (is, are) living on Elm Street, across from Langley Park.

17. Politics (is, are) the practice of managing affairs of public policy.

18. The United States (is, are) sending a delegate to the peace conference.

19. The West Indies (is, are) a part of the world I'd like to visit.

20. Home economics I (is, are) a challenging course, covering many important topics.

Titles and Groups of Words. Any group of words referring to a single thing or thought is used with a singular verb. For example, a singular verb is used after the title or name of a country, book, play, film, musical composition, or dance.

The Navajos was written by Ruth M. Underhill.
The Netherlands is small but prosperous.

Words of Amount and Time. Words or phrases that express periods of time, fractions, weights, measures, and amounts of money are usually singular.

Fifty dollars *is* more than *I* wanted to pay.
Half of the book *is* well written.

If a prepositional phrase separates the subject from the verb, the verb is singular if its subject is meant as a single thing. The verb is plural if its subject is meant as a plural thing.

Five pounds of flour *was* what I ordered.
Five bags of mail *were* delivered.

Choosing the Correct Verb Form. Underline the correct form of the verb in each sentence below.

1. Half of the state (is, are) mountainous.

2. What most people want (is, are) understanding from their friends.

3. *The Rest of the Robots* (was, were) written by Isaac Asimov.

4. Two days (is, are) not long enough to see all the sights in Lexington, Kentucky.

5. Three-fourths of Ray's free time (is, are) devoted to writing poetry.

6. The Union of Soviet Socialist Republics (is, are) another name for Russia.

7. Eighty-nine cents (is, are) too much to pay for a grapefruit.

8. "The gods help them that help themselves" (is, are) a quotation from Aesop.

9. Five pounds of potatoes (is, are) more than we need for the potato salad.

10. Two weeks (is, are) too little time to spend planning your science fair project.

11. Two cups of flour (was, were) called for in the recipe.

12. "Mehitabel and Her Kittens," by Don Marquis, (is, are) Cheryl's favorite poem.

13. Over two-thirds of the earth (is, are) covered by oceans.

14. Three pounds of coffee (is, are) what Mrs. Means bought today.

15. "Base Details" (is, are) a poem by Siegfried Sassoon.

16. Seventy-five cents (is, are) what the tickets for the roller coaster cost.

17. "Bold Fenian Men" (is, are) a beautiful Irish folk song.

18. Three yards of material (was, were) needed to make Greg's costume.

19. *Ring of Bright Water*, a book about otters, (was, were) written by Gavin Maxwell.

20. "It takes a great person to make a good listener" (is, are) what Arthur Helps said.

Relative Pronouns

A relative pronoun agrees with its antecedent in number. If the antecedent is singular, the relative pronoun is singular. If the antecedent is plural, the pronoun is plural. Usually, the meaning of the sentence shows you which word is the antecedent.

Alabama is a *band* that *plays* country music. (singular)
These are the *women* who *attend* West Point. (plural)
Libby is the only *one* of the drummers who also *plays* the piano. (singular)
England and France are among the *countries* that *support* the treaty. (plural)

Choosing the Correct Form of the Verb. In each of the following sentences, underline the correct form of the verb to be used with the relative pronoun.

1. Is Cora the person who (helps, help) Ms. Rogers in the chemistry lab?

2. These are the children who (is, are) in the nursery school.

3. Ms. Thornton is one of the women who (is, are) being considered for the position of Superintendant of Schools.

4. That is one of the articles that usually (appears, appear) in the San Diego paper.

5. There are many people in our town who (hopes, hope) that the building will be declared an historic landmark.

6. Maria is the first student who (has, have) ever gotten a perfect score on that exam.

7. Art is one person who (is, are) always ready to help others.

8. These are some stamps that (is, are) worth adding to your collection.

9. Alice is the only one of my friends who (has, have) been to Europe.

10. That philodendron is the only one of Pat's flowers that (grows, grow) well inside.

11. Amoeba are one-celled animals that (is, are) found in fresh and salt water.

12. Peter is the only one of my cousins who (lives, live) on the family farm.

13. Mrs. White is the only one who (was, were) not home for the family reunion.

14. *Sesame Street* is the only television program that always (interests, interest) my little brother.

15. Mrs. Owen is a woman who always (seems, seem) cheerful.

16. Kate is the only member of the team who (has, have) been swimming every day.

17. An open arena that (is, are) surrounded by rising rows of seats is an amphitheater.

18. The sports equipment that Lamonte ordered (has, have) just arrived.

19. Weaving is one of the crafts that (has, have) regained popularity in recent years.

20. Eiho was the satillite that (was, were) like an enormous balloon.

21. Rwanda is one of the African countries that (has, have) suffered from the drought.

22. Alton is the only student who (is, are) eligible for competition at the state level.

23. The children who (is, are) selling lemonade live across the street.

24. The huge white pine that (was, were) struck by lightning has survived.

Choosing the Correct Verb Form. Underline the correct form of the verb in each sentence below.

EXAMPLE: The boy's books (is, <u>are</u>) in his locker.

1. One of the greatest all-around athletes (was, were) Jim Thorpe.

2. "East of the Sun and West of the Moon" (is, are) an ancient folk tale.

3. The flock of geese (was, were) flying directly over our house.

4. Four of the teachers at our school (is, are) retiring this year.

5. The pencils in the box (was, were) sharpened for the test.

6. The last of the passenger pigeons (was, were) Martha, who died in 1914.

7. The pictures Gabe drew in nursery school (is, are) on the refrigerator door.

8. Each of the lifeguards on the beach (is, are) a good swimmer.

9. Anna's morning chores in the stable (take, takes) her hours to finish.

10. The papers from the trash can (was, were) blowing in the breeze.

11. Two of Brendan's teeth (need, needs) filling.

12. All of the shades in the house (has, have) been drawn.

13. Every one of the sprinters (run, runs) faster than I do.

14. Neither Emily nor Ricardo (is, are) coming to the dance.

15. The doorbell and the telephone always (ring, rings) at the same time.

16. Parsley or green peppers (is, are) a good source of vitamin A.

17. (Here's, Here are) the lines you have to memorize for the skit.

18. Inside the palace of Versailles (is, are) the famous Hall of Mirrors.

19. Why (is, are) the newspapers stacked up on the porch?

20. Most paintings in this exhibit (don't, doesn't) belong to the museum.

21. It (doesn't, don't) make sense to take the bus all the way to Toledo.

22. (Don't, Doesn't) anyone in Jenny's class live near her?

23. A lawyer's ethics (is, are) central to the practice of his profession.

24. Half of the yogurt we made (is, are) gone.

25. Howard is the neighbor who (like, likes) to play football with us.

26. The platypus and the echidna, both of which live in Australia, (is, are) the only mammals that lay eggs.

27. Either Kevin or his parents (has, have) the plane tickets.

28. Some of the questions on the economics study sheet (requires, require) long answers.

The Pronoun as Subject

The nominative form of the pronoun is used as the subject of a verb. The problem of which pronoun form to use as subject arises chiefly when the subject is compound. To decide which pronoun form to use in a compound subject, *try each part of the subject by itself with the verb.*

> Mary and (I, me) went to the tryouts. (Mary went; I went, *not* me went)
> The Wilsons and (we, us) gave a party. (The Wilsons gave; we gave, *not* us gave)

The Predicate Pronoun. The verb *be* is a linking verb. It links the noun, pronoun, or adjective following it to the subject. A pronoun so linked is called a **predicate pronoun**. **The nominative pronoun form is used as a predicate pronoun.** The problem of which form to use in a predicate pronoun occurs mainly after the verb *be*.

> It was *I* who spoke to you.
> It could have been *they*.

Choosing the Correct Pronoun. Underline the correct pronoun in each sentence below:

> EXAMPLE: The Johnsons and (<u>we</u>, us) are going to the movie.

1. Tom is sure that the winner will be (he, him).

2. Fred and (me, I) cooked the pancakes for the fund-raising breakfast.

3. It was (he, him) who answered the letter we sent.

4. His cousins and (he, him) play in a band together.

5. It could have been (them, they) who cleaned off the tennis court.

6. (Him, He) and the argonauts went on a quest for the Golden Fleece.

7. Erica and (her, she) played a duet in the piano recital.

8. It is (her, she) who is going to build the cage for the hamsters.

9. It could have been (he, him) who intercepted the message.

10. Arthur Sullivan and (he, him) wrote many comic operas.

11. It was (us, we) whom you heard laughing on the porch last night.

12. Nancy and (I, me) played chess for several hours yesterday.

13. It must have been (her, she) who rang the doorbell.

14. Laura and (him, he) belong to the debate club and the speech team.

15. It is (us, we) who made the phone call to Amarillo.

16. We and (they, them) plan a vacation in California this summer.

17. Bob and (me, I) are doing research on recycling methods.

18. Humphrey Bogart and (she, her) starred in several films together.

19. That could be (him, he) waiting at the door of the museum.

20. Was it (they, them) you saw at the volleyball game on Wednesday?

The Pronoun as Object (I)

The objective pronoun form is used as the direct or indirect object. The problem of which pronoun form to use as object of the verb arises chiefly when the object is compound. To decide which pronoun to use with a compound object, *try each part of the object by itself with the verb.*

DIRECT OBJECT: My question irritated Mr. O'Conner and (he, him). (irritated Mr. O'Conner; irritated him, *not* he)

INDIRECT OBJECT: Ask Katie and (I, me) your question. (ask Katie; ask me, *not* ask I)

Choosing the Correct Pronoun. Underline the correct pronoun in each sentence.

EXAMPLE: Tell David and (I, <u>me</u>) your birthdate.

1. Please tell Evan and (me, I) if you will be late for the meeting.

2. Ask Don and (she, her) all your questions.

3. Give your brother and (I, me) an honest answer.

4. The mayor presented the Senator and (him, he) keys to the city.

5. Tell Vivian and (she, her) that we're too late to see the beginning of the movie.

6. Mrs. Barnes asked Julio and (me, I) to help landscape her yard.

7. Mr. Riley, who works at the planetarium, gave Joe and (I, me) a tour.

8. Thank Rolanda and (she, her) for their help in developing the pictures.

9. The carnival worker handed both Jane and (him, he) free tickets.

10. At least offer (he, him) and (me, I) some encouragement.

11. Long hours of commuting tire both Mom and (he, him).

12. Save the Garcias and (us, we) seats in the auditorium.

13. Will you recommend (her, she) and (I, me) for the training program?

14. Please play Bonita and (I, me) something on your guitar.

15. The librarian showed Josh and (she, her) some jazz records from the 1930's.

16. You'd better consult the Daleys and (them, they) before you continue with the repairs on the driveway.

17. The players on the park district soccer team included John and (me, I).

18. Ask Dwight and (she, her) if they can come with us to the antique auto show.

19. Don't give Bryan and (I, me) any more tickets to sell for the play.

20. Please tell Sonia and (him, he) that anecdote again.

21. I'm sure that both Kristen and (I, me) can help at the sale.

22. Grandmother gave Lucinda and (me, I) quilts she had made herself.

23. Ms. Moran gave (him, he) and (she, her) several books about Peru.

24. The photographer sent my brother and (I, me) all of the pictures.

25. Did Marlene write (he, him) or her aunt about the trip to Yellowstone?

The Pronoun as Object (II)

When the pronoun is the object of a preposition, the objective form is always used. Problems may arise when the object is compound. To decide which pronoun to use, *try each part of the object by itself with the preposition.*

Mr. Jones lent camping equipment to Ann and (I, me). (to Ann; to me, *not* to I)

The Pronoun Used with a Noun. In a construction such as *we girls* or *us boys*, the use of the noun determines the case form of the pronoun.

We girls made our costumes for the Halloween party. (*girls* is the subject of *made*; the nominative pronoun is therefore required.)

To decide which pronoun form to use in the construction such as *we girls*, try the pronoun by itself with the verb or preposition.

The hours on the job are too long for (we, us) students. (for us, *not* for we)

Choosing the Correct Pronoun. In each sentence below, underline the correct form of the pronoun.

1. Just between you and (me, I), I'm afraid of flying in an airplane.

2. Miss Miller doesn't live far from you and (she, her).

3. There has been a good relationship between the Flynns and (us, we) for years.

4. Give the results of our survey to Alice and (him, he).

5. The money will be divided among the Ortegas, the Wojciks, and (we, us).

6. The principal congratulated (us, we) students on the results of the paper drive.

7. The extra yearbook work was divided among (we, us) editors.

8. The master of ceremonies had a special prize for John and (he, him).

9. There are many famous stories about Dr. Watson and (him, he).

10. The credit for winning the game goes to all of (we, us) players.

11. I received phone calls from Sarah and (her, she) last night.

12. Everyone was on time for the computer lab demonstration except (we, us) two.

13. Please show your sketches of the mountains to Paul and (he, him).

14. Before the show, one of the actors sat down beside Joy and (me, I).

15. The prize-winning Angora rabbits were raised by Gino and (us, we).

16. The basketball center towered above Bob and (she, her).

17. Tony Awards were presented to Marsha Norman and (her, she).

18. A few thin, wispy clouds drifted lazily above Saundra and (I, me).

19. The baseball landed just beyond (us, we) spectators.

20. The reporters formed a circle around the inventor and (him, he).

Who and Whom

Who and *whom* are pronouns that are used either to ask questions or to introduce adjective or noun clauses. When used to ask questions, *who* and *whom* are called **interrogative pronouns**. When used to relate an adjective clause to the noun that it modifies, *who* and *whom* are called **relative pronouns**.

INTERROGATIVE PRONOUN: *Who* wrote the candidate's acceptance speech?
RELATIVE PRONOUN: Ms. Walker is a scientist *who* does cancer research.

Who is the nominative form of the pronoun. It is used as the subject of the verb or as a predicate pronoun.
Who invented baseball? (*Who* is the subject.)
We were not sure *who* that was. (*who* is a predicate pronoun.)
Whom is the objective form of the pronoun. It is used as the direct object or as the object of a preposition.
Whom shall I ask to the dance? (*Whom* is the direct object.)
Wanda was the person to *whom* the package was sent. (*whom* is the object of the preposition *to*.)

Using *Who* and *Whom* Correctly. Underline the standard form of the pronoun in each sentence.

1.   (Who, Whom) will be the captain of this year's soccer team?

2.   (Who, Whom) do you know in Denver, Colorado?

3.   Maggie Smith is one actress (who, whom) I respect very much.

4.   Ernest Hemingway, one of many American writers (who, whom) lived in Paris in the 1920's, wrote *The Old Man and the Sea*.

5.   Samantha was the little girl for (who, whom) the story was originally written.

6.   (Who, Whom) did the receiver pass the ball to?

7.   The scientists (who, whom) measure the force of earthquakes are called *seismologists*.

8.   Most of the students figured out (who, whom) the villain of the novel really was.

9.   Has the coach decided (who, whom) the captain of the team will be?

10.   Pablo Picasso was the painter (who, whom) we learned most about.

11.   The librarian (who, whom) sits in the reference area will be happy to assist you.

12.   The musician (who, whom) we saw plays for the Detroit Symphony Orchestra.

13.   (Who, Whom) has been chosen to represent our school at the mathematics competition next month?

14.   Is Marco the person with (who, whom) you played the duet?

15.   Cervantes was the author (who, whom) wrote *Don Quixote*.

16.   Robert E. Peary and Frederick Cook were the two explorers (who, whom) both claimed to have reached the North Pole first.

17.   The people (who, whom) we sat next to at the game had to leave early.

18.   The manager is the person (who, whom) I need to see.

Other Problems with Pronouns

Pronouns in Comparisons. Sometimes a comparison is made by using a clause that begins with *than* or *as*.

> You are better at French *than I am*.
> Does Jack have as many pets *as she has*?

Sometimes the final clause in the comparison is left incomplete.

> You are better at French *than I* (*am*).
> Does Jack have as many pets *as she* (*has*)?

To decide which pronoun form to use in an incomplete comparison, complete the comparison.

> Ellen saves more of her paycheck *than* (*I, me*).
>   (Ellen saves more of her paycheck *than I save*.)

Compound Personal Pronouns. Compound personal pronouns are used only when their antecedents appear in the same sentence.

> **NONSTANDARD:** The tickets were meant for ourselves.
> **STANDARD:** The tickets were meant for us.

Choosing the Correct Pronoun. Underline the standard form of the pronoun in each sentence.

> **EXAMPLE:** Marge is a better letter writer than (<u>I</u>, me).

1. Robin is a better archer than (he, him).

2. No age restrictions apply to (you, yourself).

3. Betty wrote a better monologue than (me, I).

4. Jim ran more hurdles in less time than (I, me).

5. You have a longer writing assignment than (me, I).

6. The quarterback hasn't trained as hard as (me, I).

7. Meg is a better artist than (he, him).

8. We have as long a vacation as (they, them).

9. Does that five-speed bicycle belong to (yourself, you)?

10. Francis makes more money than (I, me).

11. You always have a bigger breakfast than (we, us).

12. No one works harder at her lessons than (she, her).

13. Marina is nearly two years older than (I, me).

14. Does this mandolin belong to (you, yourself)?

15. You have a better chance of winning the photography award than (I, me).

16. Nancy has as much athletic talent as (they, them).

17. In our class play Tim was a better actor than (he, him).

18. The poem that Terence read was written for (me, myself).

Pronouns and Antecedents

A pronoun agrees with its antecedent in number, gender, and person. If the antecedent is singular, a singular pronoun is required. If the antecedent is plural, a plural pronoun is required. The following antecedents are referred to by singular pronouns: *anybody*, *anyone*, *each*, *either*, *everybody*, *everyone*, *neither*, *nobody*, *one*, *somebody*, *someone*.

Each of the boys has *his* own savings account.

Singular antecedents joined by *or* or *nor* are referred to by a singular pronoun.

Neither John *nor* Dave could find his ticket.

Collective nouns may take either a singular or plural pronoun, depending on the meaning of the sentence.

The cast is having *its* picture taken.
The cast quickly took *their* places onstage.

Choosing the Right Pronoun. Underline the correct pronoun in each sentence.

EXAMPLE: Either Frank or Bob will give you (his, their) ticket.

1. Neither Mary nor Laura has turned in (their, her) report.

2. Anybody can learn to set up (their, his) own tent.

3. Each of the states sends (its, their) two senators to Washington.

4. Neither Vito nor Dana can give (his, their) ecology report today.

5. Anyone can join the drama club if (they, he) is really interested.

6. The team can't play (their, its) best on a muddy field.

7. Either Bill or Tony will lend you (his, their) book.

8. Everyone should do (their, his) best work on the woodworking project.

9. George wants to go into politics; he finds (it, them) exciting.

10. Everyone should buckle (his, their) seatbelt before the car starts.

11. Some of the team are wearing (their, his) new helmets.

12. Every class officer will do (her, their) best.

13. Neither Antonio nor Juan wants (their, his) painting to be sold at the exhibit.

14. Some of the vanilla has lost (their, its) flavor.

15. Everybody will receive (his, their) own copy of the driver training handbook.

16. Someone will be disappointed about (his, their) flat bicycle tire.

17. One should not worry too much about (his, their) past mistakes.

18. Each of the clubs will present (their, its) own program.

19. Has anyone lost (his, their) school jacket?

20. Nobody plays (their, his) best when the humidity is very high.

Indefinite Reference

To avoid confusion for the reader, every personal pronoun should refer clearly to a definite antecedent.

INDEFINITE: They won't let you in until the members of the band are seated.
BETTER: The ushers won't let you in until the members of the band are seated.
INDEFINITE: They say that *All Creatures Great and Small* is a good book.
BETTER: That book reviewer said that *All Creatures Great and Small* is a good book.

Avoiding Indefinite References. Revise the sentences below to remove all indefinite pronoun references.

EXAMPLE: It says in the book that Elizabeth I was a great queen.
BETTER: The book says that Elizabeth I was a great queen.

1. You should find out your grade if they will let you.

_____

2. On the roller coaster, you may be surprised how fast it is.

_____

3. It says in the article that high school enrollment is up again.

_____

4. In the preface it explains how they used to live on homesteads in the 1800's.

_____

_____

5. Mark wants to be an actor because it's such an exciting life.

_____

6. We hailed the taxi driver, but it kept going.

_____

7. In the nineteenth century, you had to work a twelve-hour day.

_____

8. Mrs. Jones writes them letters about everything.

_____

9. In some parts of the West, you get very little rainfall.

_____

10. They said that you need to get special permission to bring a visitor to school.

_____

_____

Ambiguous Reference

Ambiguous means "having two or more possible meanings." The reference of a pronoun is ambiguous if the pronoun may refer back to more than one word. Ambiguous pronouns confuse the reader because the meaning is not clear.

Fernando told Tom his book was lost. (whose book?)
Janet gave Maria her picture. (whose picture?)

Avoiding Ambiguous References. Revise the sentences below to remove all ambiguous pronoun references.

EXAMPLE: Add the noodles to the casseroles after cooking them.
BETTER: After cooking the noodles, add them to the casseroles.

1. When Gina spoke with Ms. Lin, she was very polite. _____

_____

2. After we took the dish from the beautifully carved box, it broke. _____

_____

3. We removed the pictures from the walls and cleaned them. _____

_____

4. The wizard Merlin told the young King Arthur that the sword was his. _____

_____

5. Melanie took the turtle out of the terrarium and washed it. _____

_____

6. Jane told Cecilia that she had won first prize. _____

_____

7. I put my plant on the shelf, but it still didn't look right. _____

_____

8. Mr. Peterson's article was in the magazine, but I didn't read it. _____

_____

9. On his bicycle Ken followed the rock star's bus until it broke down. _____

_____

10. Please take the meat out of the oven and carve it. _____

_____

Review: Pronoun Usage

Choosing the Correct Pronoun. Underline the correct pronoun in each sentence.

    EXAMPLE: Millie and (<u>I</u>, me) are going shopping tomorrow.

1. The best athlete in the gym class is (she, her).

2. The stretcher was carried by the medic and (he, him).

3. The photographs of the exchange students and (we, us) are blurred.

4. Cindy and (he, him) are taking a class in mime.

5. Barry showed (I, me) his attempts at pottery making.

6. I need to ask the receptionist or (her, she) where the office is located.

7. That secret was supposed to be kept between you and (I, me).

8. A bill for a tape recorder that we didn't buy was mistakenly sent to (we, us).

9. Yvonne is a faster jogger than (I, me), but I have more endurance.

10. The packages were to be delivered to (us, ourselves).

11. Either Bud or Larry left (his, their) calculator at my house.

12. Neither Robert Heinlein nor Ray Bradbury has (his, their) picture on the cover.

13. All of the knives need to have (its, their) blades sharpened.

14. None of the neighbors on our block lets (his or her, their) dog loose.

15. One of the members of the team earned (his or her, their) letter this week.

Avoiding Ambiguous and Indefinite References. Revise the sentences below to remove all indefinite and ambiguous pronoun references.

    EXAMPLE: They now have summer dresses on sale.

    Sears will be putting summer clothes on sale in July.

1. Be sure to exercise regularly and keep it up. _____

_____

2. Lorraine wanted to order egg rolls but they hadn't opened yet. _____

_____

3. Ralph's horse balked at the fence and broke his leg. _____

_____

4. The dog and cat were fighting and it started snarling. _____

_____

5. We went to the park to see the ducks, but they wouldn't let us in. _____

_____

Using Adjectives and Adverbs Correctly

Many adverbs are formed by adding *-ly* to adjectives: *careful—carefully.* However, some adverbs have two forms that are correct.

Dress *warm.*   Dress *warmly.*
Go *slow*!   Go *slowly*!
Sing *loud.*   Sing *loudly.*

Confusion sometimes arises because adverbs such as the ones in the first column are also used as adjectives: a *warm* room, a *slow* trip, a *loud* voice.

Most of the words that may be either adjectives or adverbs have one syllable. Adjectives of two or more syllables almost never have the same form for the adverb.

NONSTANDARD: The driver moved *careful* through the streets.
STANDARD: The driver moved *carefully* through the streets. (adverb)
STANDARD: A *careful* driver has fewer accidents. (adjectives)

Choosing the Right Modifier. Underline the correct form in each sentence below.

EXAMPLE: Susan mended her torn jeans (careful, <u>carefully</u>).

1. Thomas Paine's pamphlets called (angry, angrily) for the colonies to revolt.
2. Jacques Cousteau made his way (careful, carefully) back into the boat.
3. Carving a cameo is (painstaking, painstakingly) work.
4. Louisa completed the translation (easy, easily).
5. The little girl gazed (shy, shyly) at the President.
6. Sheila's injury looks (bad, badly).
7. The eye blinks (automatic, automatically) every two to ten seconds.
8. Did Bogart speak (threatening, threateningly) to Peter Lorre in *The Maltese Falcon*?
9. The dean nodded (cordial, cordially) to me when I approached him.
10. Thomas Edison worked (constant, constantly) day and night.
11. Sally seemed (nervous, nervously) as she approached the microphone.
12. The phones rang (noisy, noisily) in the newsroom.
13. A coral reef develops (slow, slowly) from the hard skeletons of tiny sea animals.
14. Mary will (certain, certainly) want to hear herself interviewed on the radio.
15. The two boys talked (loud, loudly) about who would win the Super Bowl.
16. Ann's first painting was displayed (prominent, prominently) above the fireplace.
17. Pam was dressed (outlandish, outlandishly) in a clown suit and a wig.
18. The lecturer peered (uneasy, uneasily) at the audience.
19. Ms. Russo (quick, quickly) made her way through the crowded hall.
20. Do all the stories you tell end so (sad, sadly)?

Adjectives with Linking Verbs

Forms of the verb *be* are always used as linking verbs. Other verbs such as *look*, *sound*, *appear*, *feel*, *smell*, *stay*, and *grow* may be used as either action verbs followed by adverbs, or as linking verbs followed by adjectives. To decide whether a verb is used to link or show action, try substituting a form of *be*. If the sentence still makes sense, the verb is a linking verb and is followed by an adjective.

> **EXAMPLE:** Cynthia seems rather (*shy*, shyly).
> (*Cynthia is shyly* does not make sense. *Cynthia is shy* makes sense; *seems* is a linking verb here.)
> Cynthia looked (shy, *shyly*) at the mayor.
> (*was* does not make sense with either modifier; *looked* is an action verb here.)

Choosing the Right Modifier. Underline the correct form in each sentence below.

1. The people of Pompeii grew (nervous, nervously) when Mount Vesuvius began to rumble and shake.

2. Under the heavy blanket I stayed (warm, warmly) all night.

3. The garlic bread smells (good, well).

4. The musician sounded his trumpet (loud, loudly).

5. Mrs. Barnes works (good, well) with many people.

6. Bill looks (tired, tiredly) after his ordeal.

7. The lemonade tasted (good, well) on that hot night.

8. Kristin analyzed the movie (careful, carefully) and decided it was too unrealistic.

9. The campers stayed (cozy, cozily) by the fire all night.

10. I've learned to identify various kinds of minerals by testing them (careful, carefully).

11. The little girl looked (cautious, cautiously) to the right and left.

12. Bob sometimes loses his temper, but he never remains (angry, angrily) very long.

13. Karen tasted the hot chili (cautious, cautiously).

14. Marta slept (restless, restlessly) after watching the scary movie.

15. The mayor seems (anxious, anxiously) when talking to reporters.

16. Don sometimes becomes (angry, angrily) when he's teased about his nickname.

17. After reading by the fire, Ken became very (sleepy, sleepily).

18. The driving instructor seemed (uneasy, uneasily) when he first got into the car.

19. Pam always remains (calm, calmly) under pressure.

20. The speech contestant looked (uneasy, uneasily) at the judges.

21. Juan looks (good, well) in his costume.

22. Gregory appears (eager, eagerly) to take on additional responsibilities.

This, These, Them, That, and Those. *This* and *that* modify singular words. *These* and *those* modify plural words. The words *kind*, *sort*, and *type* require a singular modifier. *Those* may be used as either a pronoun or an adjective. *Them* is always a pronoun.

> *This* sort of shoes is too tight for me. (Not *these sort*)
> *Those* are good books. (pronoun)
> *Those* books are good. (adjective)

Bad-Badly and Good-Well. *Bad* is always used after linking verbs. (Mr. Smith *felt* bad. The milk *smelled* bad). *Badly* is used after action verbs. (She *sang* badly.)
Good is used only as an adjective to modify nouns and pronouns. *Well* is an adjective when it means "in good health, of good appearance, or satisfactory." *Well* is used as an adverb when it means that an action was performed properly and expertly.

Using *This, These, Them, That,* and *Those.* Underline the correct word.

EXAMPLE: (<u>That</u>, Those) kind of pizza is my favorite.

1. Marcy likes (that, those) sort of television program.
2. (This, These) type of boots is good for walking through slush.
3. Doug put (those, them) spoons in the drawer.
4. (That, Those) kind of abrupt answer irritates me.
5. Don't you like (this, these) kind of Danish cheese?
6. Elizabeth is always angered by (that, those) type of question.
7. Why should you worry about (that, those) kind of remark?
8. Please put (those, them) socket wrenches in the garage.
9. Todd prefers (this, these) sort of ethnic food.
10. (That, Those) type of story is my favorite.

Using *Bad-Badly* and *Good-Well.* Underline the correct form.

EXAMPLE: Mike looks (<u>bad</u>, badly).

1. Mrs. Heinz felt (good, well) about her research grant.
2. The potato salad was left unrefrigerated and now tastes (bad, badly).
3. Although it cannot fly, the penguin swims very (good, well).
4. The news report about the Mideast sounded (bad, badly).
5. Don't feel (bad, badly) about your mistake; learn from it instead.
6. In spite of many lessons Jim plays golf (bad, badly).
7. The lawn mower works (good, well) now that Corinne has sharpened it.
8. The actors spoke their lines so (bad, badly) that the audience began to laugh.
9. The children behaved (bad, badly) on the long flight from Boston to Miami.
10. The whole house smells (good, well) because we're making applesauce.

Usage Problems (II)

Fewer and Less. *Fewer* is used to describe things that can be counted. *Less* refers to quantity or degree.

> There are fewer students taking Latin now.
> This bulb will give less light.

The Double Negative. A double negative occurs when a negative word is added to a statement that is already negative. The double negative is nonstandard usage.

NONSTANDARD: Tom didn't have no book.
STANDARD: Tom didn't have any book.

Hardly, used with a negative word, is nonstandard.

NONSTANDARD: There wasn't hardly any money in my checking account.
STANDARD: There was hardly any money in my checking account.

Using *Fewer* and *Less*. Underline the correct word in each sentence below.

1. Nixon received slightly (fewer, less) votes than Kennedy in the 1960 election.

2. Mark has (fewer, less) fear of the water than he used to have.

3. This new calculator will cause you (fewer, less) mistakes.

4. An adult has (fewer, less) bones than a baby because some bones fuse together.

5. Beth feels (fewer, less) anxiety now that she exercises regularly.

6. We have (fewer, less) milk than the recipe calls for.

7. Marilyn has (fewer, less) worries than anyone else I know.

8. There was (fewer, less) rainfall yesterday than we had expected.

9. There are (fewer, less) cases of measles now that children receive shots to protect them.

10. Home computers may result in (fewer, less) people commuting to jobs.

Avoiding the Double Negative. In the following sentences, underline the correct form.

1. Water doesn't contain (any, no) calories.

2. There (was, wasn't) hardly enough cheese left for lunch.

3. The residents of Mackinac Island don't allow (any, no) automobiles on their streets.

4. John doesn't know (anything, nothing) about hang-gliding.

5. I (could, couldn't) hardly see the stage without my glasses.

6. There (was, wasn't) hardly anything Charlie said that wasn't funny.

7. According to the driver, Larry doesn't have (a, no) bus pass.

8. We (had, hadn't) hardly enough room to stand on the crowded subway.

9. Nora doesn't care (anything, nothing) about pro football.

10. I don't see (anything, nothing) moving in the bushes, but I do hear something.

Comparisons

Comparative and Superlative. The comparative form of a modifier is used to compare only two things; the superlative is used to compare three or more things. The comparative is made either by adding an *-er* ending or by using the word *more*. The superlative is formed either by adding *-est* or by using the word *most*. Never use *more* or *most* if you have already added the *-er* or *-est* ending.

Illogical Comparisons. When an individual is compared with the rest of the group, always use the word *other* or the word *else*.

> Jim is more vocal than any of the officers.
>   (Is Jim an officer, too?)
> Jim is more vocal than any of the *other* officers. (*other* tells you he is.)

State both parts of a comparison completely if the meaning is not clear.

> I listen to the radio more than my sister.
>   (I listen to my sister? My sister listens to the radio?)
> I listen to the radio more than my sister listens to it. (logical)

Using Comparisons. Circle the mistakes below. Place the correct form in the blank.

1. Do you like *Time* or *Newsweek* best? _____

2. Justin is more taller than Nicholas. _____

3. Ms. Gordon is the most busiest of the three camp counselors. _____

4. Of the two schools, Lincolnwood has the biggest enrollment. _____

5. The most commonest last name in the United States is Smith. _____

6. Which of the two candidates do you like best? _____

7. Of all the breeds of dogs, Tony thinks spaniels are friendlier. _____

8. What would be the more interesting job in the world? _____

Avoiding Illogical Comparisons. Add a word or words needed to make the following sentences logical rather than illogical comparisons.

1. Rex is better trained than Sandra's dog. _____

2. Beth watches television more than Ann. _____

3. Dave has more endurance than any swimmer I know. _____

4. Mike is more talkative than anybody in the club. _____

5. Ms. Persons commutes farther than any teacher in the school. _____

6. Mr. Bucks is richer than anyone in our town. _____

7. Paul finds serving is more difficult than any skill needed in tennis. _____

8. I clean my room more than my brother. _____

Choosing the Right Modifier. Underline the correct form in each sentence below.

    EXAMPLE: We walked (brisk, <u>briskly</u>) through the forest.

1. Roger receives letters (regular, regularly) from his foreign pen pals.

2. You must enter the data (careful, carefully), or your results will be wrong.

3. The cab driver seemed (uncertain, uncertainly) about our destination.

4. The citrus harvest appears (meager, meagerly) this year.

5. The tourists looked (eager, eagerly) at Old Faithful, waiting for it to erupt.

6. Lynn looked (tired, tiredly) after her first day on the job.

7. (This, These) sort of granola bar is my favorite.

8. John felt (well, good) about scoring the winning run.

9. Surprisingly, the sandwiches looked (good, well) before we ate them.

10. From what I heard on the radio, the accident sounded (bad, badly).

11. Do you prefer (that, those) type of guitar string?

12. Elephants are intelligent and respond to commands very (good, well).

13. The picture appeared (crooked, crookedly) from where we stood.

14. Penicillin was discovered (accidental, accidentally).

15. Alchemists were people who tried (diligent, diligently) to turn base metals into gold.

16. Doesn't the library have (any, no) books on mountain climbing?

17. (Fewer, Less) people live on the farms now than ever before.

18. No one (was, wasn't) waiting at the bus stop when I got there.

19. I don't think (anyone, no one) signed up for the clean-up committee.

20. Which burns up (fewer, less) calories—jogging or jumping rope?

Using Comparisons. Find the mistakes in the following sentences. If an extra word has been used, cross it out. If a comparative or superlative has been used incorrectly, circle it and place the correct form in the blank.

    EXAMPLE: Ken is the (most) intelligent of the two boys. _____ *more* _____

1. Of all the fifty states, Alaska has the smaller number of people. _____

2. Which do you like better—Chinese, Italian, or Mexican food? _____

3. What is the most tallest breed of dog? _____

4. Considering all of the contestants, I deserved to win more. _____

5. Getting a blood test hurts lesser than getting a shot. _____

Words Commonly Confused

The following words are often confused.

accept, except   To *accept* is "to agree or to receive something willingly." To *except* is to "exclude or omit." As a preposition, *except* means "but" or "excluding."

agree to, with, on   You agree *to* something, such as a plan. You agree *with* someone else; or something such as spinach does not agree *with* you. You agree with others *on* a course of action.

altogether, all together   *Altogether* means "entirely" or "on the whole." *All together* means that all parts of a group are considered together.

amount, number   *Amount* is used to indicate a total sum of things. It is usually used to refer to items that cannot be counted. *Number* is used to refer to items that can be counted.

angry at, with   You are angry *with* a person and angry *at* a thing.

bring, take   *Bring* means motion or movement towards someone or some place; *take* means motion or movement away from someone or some place.

differ from, with   One thing or person differs *from* another in characteristics. You differ *with* someone when you disagree with him or her.

imply, infer   A speaker or writer suggests or *implies* something. The reader or listener comes to a conclusion or *infers* something on the basis of what he or she sees and hears.

it's, its   *It's* means "it is." *Its* is a possessive pronoun.

their, they're, there   *Their* is a possessive pronoun. *They're* means "they are." *There*, like *here*, refers to a place.

Choosing the Right Words. Underline the standard form.

1.   We put the coins (altogether, all together) in the desk drawer.

2.   Cucumbers have never (agreed to, agreed with, agreed on) me.

3.   Eva is always willing to (accept, except) constructive criticism.

4.   Sandy is not really (angry at, angry with) Robin.

5.   I (differ from, differ with) you somewhat on that issue.

6.   Then the car broke down, but that is (altogether, all together) another story.

7.   The mother cat carried her kitten by the scruff of (its, it's) neck.

8.   The American colonies did not (agree to, agree on, agree with) the British policies.

9.   Mom is (taking, bringing) the suit to the cleaners today.

10.   Some voters (implied, inferred) that the President was going to raise taxes.

11.   The students wondered if (they're, there, their) teacher would give them a quiz.

12.   Tony's New England accent (differs from, differs with) Gwen's Southern accent.

13.   Do you think that (their, they're, there) brother is really Harrison Ford?

14.   (Its, It's) time to set up our telescope to observe the comet.

15.   Many home computers do not cost a large (amount, number) of money.

The following words are often misused:

all of   The *of* is unnecessary except before pronouns.

all right   The misspelling *alright* is nonstandard usage. The two words are separate.

anywhere, nowhere, somewhere, anyway *Anywheres*, *nowheres*, *somewheres*, and *anyways* are nonstandard.

had of, off of   The *of* is unnecessary and nonstandard.

kind of a, sort of a   The *a* is unnecessary and nonstandard.

majority   This word can be used only with items that can be counted. It is nonstandard if used in speaking of time or distance.

seldom ever   The *ever* is unnecessary and nonstandard. Use *seldom*, *very seldom*, or *hardly ever* instead.

Identifying Misused Words. Underline the standard form.

1.   Tom had the flu, but now he is feeling (all right, alright).

2.   (All, All of) the students thought that the novel had a bizarre ending.

3.   Everett (seldom ever, seldom) eats in the cafeteria.

4.   (Most, The majority) of the road to Springfield is a four-lane highway.

5.   Mother ordered the dog (off of, off) the sofa.

6.   If you (had, had of) asked, I would have helped you.

7.   Susan can't find her bracelet (anywhere, anywheres).

8.   What (sort of a, sort of) movie do you like best?

9.   I have looked all over the house and the yard, but my glasses are (nowheres, nowhere) to be found.

10.   (All, all of) the members of the emergency room staff were kept very busy last night.

11.   (The majority, Most) of January was extremely cold.

12.   Chris thought she had left her wallet (somewheres, somewhere) in the library.

13.   (Alright, All right), I'll go to the concert with you.

14.   One of the limbs fell (off, off of) the tree outside my window.

15.   We (hardly ever, seldom ever) miss the summer concerts in the park.

16.   The water was cold, but we swam (anyway, anyways).

17.   I can't decide what (kind of, kind of a) restaurant to go to for my party.

18.   The band director gave written directions to (all of, all) us so there wouldn't be any last minute confusion.

19.   It was the (sort of, sort of a) discussion that involved everyone.

20.   Molly hurt her knee and couldn't walk for (most, the majority) of the week.

Review: The Right Word

Choose the standard form from the two choices given for each sentence below. Underline the standard form.

EXAMPLE: The family was (altogether, <u>all together</u>) for Christmas.

1. Our club members can't (agree with, agree on) a motto.
2. We didn't have (anywhere, anywheres) special to spend the evening.
3. The boss told her staff that it was (alright, all right) to leave early.
4. Your hypothesis is (all together, altogether) possible.
5. Andrew (seldom, seldom ever) exercises, but he seems to be in good shape.
6. There was a large (amount, number) of ants near the picnic blanket.
7. Good debaters never get (angry at, angry with) one another.
8. Virgil had a (kind of, kind of a) virus last week.
9. Some sounds in Spanish (differ with, differ from) those in English.
10. Did you (bring, take) enough food for all of us?
11. What (sort of a, sort of) horse is the fastest?
12. Our coach has (excepted, accepted) a new job with a college team.
13. No one (except, accept) the immediate family is allowed.
14. All the people who enter Emile's house must remove (they're, their, there) shoes.
15. What foods did the Indians (bring, take) to the Pilgrim settlers?
16. You can fool (all of, all) the people some of the time.
17. The Jacksons forgot to (take, bring) the poles for their tent.
18. John (implied, inferred) from the letter that his sister was really enjoying college.
19. The master of ceremonies (implied, inferred) that he was nervous too.
20. (Its, It's) important to fill out applications correctly.
21. Emily Dickinson spent (most, the majority) of her life inside her father's house.
22. There were a large (amount, number) of people waiting at the railroad station.
23. Lynette (agreed to, agreed with, agreed on) babysitting every afternoon for Mrs. Jones' three children.
24. That kind of architecture is found (nowhere, nowheres) but here.
25. Suzanne answered all the questions on the PSAT (except, accept) one.
26. Jason and Brian spent (most, the majority) of the afternoon cleaning up the yard.
27. Ms. Marcuso took (all, all of) the kindergarten children to the zoo.
28. The teacher (differs from, differs with) the principal about field trip procedures.
29. Carmen was (angry at, angry with) the television because it kept going off.
30. (Anyway, Anyways), Kirk and Richard will make sure all the props are backstage.

A **common noun** is the name of a whole group of persons, places, or things. A **proper noun** is the name of an individual person, place, or thing. A **proper adjective** is an adjective formed from a proper noun.

COMMON NOUN	PROPER NOUN	PROPER ADJECTIVE
country	France	French
state	Iowa	Iowan

Proper nouns and adjectives often appear in compound words. Capitalize only the parts of compounds that are capitalized when they stand alone. Do not capitalize prefixes such as *pro-*, *in-*, and *pre-*.

Geographical Names. In a geographical name, capitalize the first letter of each word except articles and prepositions.

The article *the* appearing before a geographical name is not part of the geographical name and is therefore not capitalized.

CONTINENTS:	Europe, North America, Africa, Asia
BODIES OF WATER:	the Pacific Ocean, Lake Michigan, the Ohio River
LAND FORMS:	Mount Everest, the Rocky Mountains, the Mojave Desert
POLITICAL UNITS:	the Department of Agriculture, New York State, Lake County
PUBLIC AREAS:	Yellowstone National Park, Fort Dix, Indiana Dunes
ROADS AND HIGHWAYS:	State Street, U. S. Highway 1, the Bluegrass Parkway

Capitalizing Words Correctly. Supply capital letters where needed in the following sentences.

1. The Fallons visited the people's republic of china on their asian trip.

2. Alligators stare back at the tourists at everglades national park in florida.

3. edinburgh, scotland, is located near a body of water called the firth of forth.

4. One of the main highways in new jersey is the garden state parkway.

5. Many egyptian ruins were first unearthed by british and american archaeologists.

6. The highest mountain peak in the world is mount everest in the himalayas.

7. Who is the present secretary of the department of health and human services?

8. Which is the longer river—the nile in africa or the mississippi in the united states?

9. We drove on u. s. highway 94 all the way from detroit to chicago.

10. The cabin that we visited in the appalachian mountains dated back to the pre-revolutionary war days.

11. A cross country highway of the pre-world war II era, route 66 gradually lost its significance as tollways and interstates were built.

12. Ron has seen most of the civil war battlefields, but he has never visited gettysburg.

13. The bay of fundy, located between new brunswick and nova scotia, has tides as high as 50 feet.

14. lake titicaca, the highest navigable body of water in the world, is in bolivia.

Common Nouns in Names. A common noun that is part of a name is capitalized. A common noun used to define or refer to a proper noun is not capitalized.

PART OF THE NAME	REFERENCE OR DEFINITION
Washington State	the state of Washington
Jersey City	the city of Miami
the Berlin Wall	a wall in Berlin
the Mississippi Valley	the valley of the Mississippi

Words Modified by Proper Adjectives. The word modified by a proper adjective is not capitalized unless adjective and noun together are a geographical name.

GEOGRAPHICAL NAME	MODIFIED NOUN
the French Alps	the French language
the Irish Sea	Irish linen
Italian Riviera	Italian dressing

Capitalizing Words Correctly. Supply capital letters where needed in these sentences.

EXAMPLE: We visited the national cemetery at antietam, maryland.

1. The gaelic language is still spoken in parts of ireland.
2. We plan to take a steamboat down the mississippi river to new orleans.
3. Have you ever been to sequoia national park in california?
4. Many people have attempted to swim the english channel.
5. Barbara's aunt has lived in new york state for fifteen years.
6. A famous tourist attraction in kentucky is mammoth cave.
7. The specialty store sold french mustard, maine lobster, and danish ham.
8. I would like to trim the dress with belgian lace.
9. The state of maine touches only one other state, new hampshire.
10. The debaters have gone to a tournament in denver, colorado.
11. Two of the countries behind the iron curtain are poland and hungary.
12. Digging the canal through panama took many years.
13. We had our choice of french or russian dressing for our salads.
14. I got seasick when we went fishing in the gulf of mexico.
15. Ana has been in washington, d. c., but she's never been in the state of washington.
16. Cartier, a french navigator, discovered the st. lawrence river.
17. An irish wolfhound is one of the tallest dogs.
18. The golden gate bridge in san francisco was completed in 1937.
19. Did you know that greenland is the largest island in the world?
20. The actors in the noh play all spoke with japanese accents.

First Words. Capitalize the first word of a sentence, a direct quotation, or a line of poetry.

"How do you know you won't run when the time comes?" asked the youth.
"Run?" said the loud one; "run—of course not." He laughed.

—STEPHEN CRANE

He clasps the crag with crooked hands;
Close to the sun in lonely lands,
Ringed with the azure world, he stands.

The wrinkled sea beneath him crawls;
He watches from his mountain walls,
And like a thunderbolt he falls.

—ALFRED, LORD TENNYSON

A.D., B.C., I. Capitalize the abbreviations *A.D.* and *B.C.*, and the pronoun *I.*
B.C. and *A.D.* occur only in dates: 457 *B.C.*, *A.D.* 1215.

Capitalizing Words Correctly. Supply capital letters where needed in the items below.

EXAMPLE: Columbus discovered America in *a.d.* 1492.   *[a.d.]*

1.   "not all peanut butter," said Al dramatically, "is created equal."

2.   cold, wet leaves
     floating on moss-colored water,
     and the croaking of frogs—
     cracked bell-notes in the twilight.

—AMY LOWELL

3.   archeologists believe that Rome was settled in 753 b.c.

4.   todd said, "i wonder if Bigfoot really exists?"

5.   all that i know
        of a certain star
     is, it can throw
        (like the angled spar)
     now a dart of red
        now a dart of blue

—ROBERT BROWNING

6.   the first world conqueror, Alexander the Great, was born in 356 b.c.

7.   "who is to blame for this mistake?" asked Mr. Chung.

8.   debby said immediately, "i'll see who is at the door."

9.   hark to the whimper of the sea-gull;
     he weeps because he's not an ea-gull.
     suppose you were, you silly sea-gull,
     could you explain it to your she-gull?

—OGDEN NASH

10.   the Battle of Hastings, which resulted in the conquest of England by the Normans, occurred in a.d. 1066.

Capitalize names of parts of the country and proper adjectives derived from them. Do not capitalize directions of the compass or adjectives derived from them.

an Eastern state	a north wind
the Southern states	an eastbound flight
Southern grits	a wind from the north
West Coast	heading to the west

Capitalizing Words Correctly. Supply capital letters where needed in the following sentences. If a sentence is already correct, write **C** in the blank.

EXAMPLE: There has been a severe drought in the *W*est this year.

1.   The northeast had its coldest winter in one hundred years this year. _____

2.   Keith's grandfather moved west to Wyoming in 1920. _____

3.   From Paris, Mrs. Elliott will travel south to Madrid. _____

4.   The Senators from the southwestern states are especially interested in irrigation. _____

5.   My sister graduated from an eastern college in 1983. _____

6.   The Cumberland Mountains lie in the southeastern part of the country. _____

7.   The Barnes family has lived in the east for many years. _____

8.   Homes are often constructed differently in the north than in the south. _____

9.   By six o'clock tonight I'll be on a southbound flight to Houston. _____

10.   *Sunset Magazine* is meant especially for people living in the west. _____

11.   Why is it that so many major magazines are edited on the east coast? _____

12.   We'll take the highway leading southeast to Rome, Georgia. _____

13.   Earthquakes are more common in the west than in the eastern states. _____

14.   Henry boarded the westbound bus at 1:30 this afternoon. _____

15.   The northeastern states are home to a growing computer industry. _____

16.   The Morgans will be traveling north for their vacation. _____

17.   Cleveland is located east of Toledo. _____

18.   I've never been as far west as Cheyenne, Wyoming. _____

19.   We expect a breeze from the south tonight. _____

20.   Dave will travel southeast to Nashville next week. _____

21.   The southern part of New Jersey has numerous cranberry bogs. _____

22.   Azaleas and rhododendrons grow especially well in the south. _____

23.   Everyone in my father's family lives in the eastern part of the state. _____

24.   Where does the midwest end and the west begin? _____

Other Capitalization Rules (I)

Languages, Races, Nationalities, and Religions. Capitalize the names of languages, races, nationalities, and religions and the adjectives formed from them.

the Mongolian race	Catholic	Protestant
the Spanish language	Judaism	French
German	Methodist	Italian

Organizations and Institutions. Capitalize important words in the names of organizations, buildings, firms, schools, churches, and other institutions. Do not capitalize *and* or prepositions. Capitalize an article (*a*, *an*, or *the*) only if it appears as the first word in a name.

New Orleans Symphony	Stevens Manufacturing Company
Iowa Methodist Hospital	Lincoln Township High School
Church of the Holy Spirit	The Art Institute of Chicago
University of Iowa	Delta Air Lines

Capitalizing Words Correctly. Supply capital letters where needed .

1. The people of brazil speak portuguese.

2. The united airlines flight to chicago landed at o'hare international airport.

3. Dr. Stanley researched his book on the league of women voters at the library of congress in Washington.

4. The Talmud is a guide to the teachings of judaism.

5. My cousin plans to buy a new volkswagen sedan.

6. Ms. Martin is studying for a degree in african art.

7. Do you know the name of our delegate to the united nations?

8. The university of michigan has an outstanding law school.

9. My aunt has taught at elizabeth seton high school for many years.

10. Have you bought tickets for the concert by the philadelphia symphony orchestra?

11. There was an error in my bill from the jordan department store.

12. The delegates included members of the protestant, catholic, and jewish faiths.

13. Bill has taken a job with the chrysler corporation in detroit.

14. Nina speaks english at school and spanish at home.

15. Some people in switzerland speak french, while others speak german or italian.

16. Dr. Lewy is researching depression at the national institutes of health.

17. Wayne attended the university of illinois between 1980 and 1984.

18. The star of the rose bowl is now a patient at mercy hospital.

19. Tom is traveling to texas on a greyhound bus.

20. Some of my ancestors were korean, while some were japanese.

Titles of Persons. Capitalize words that show rank, office, or profession when they are used with a person's name.

Doctor Jones   Senator Parsons   Colonel Bentley
Corporal Thomas   Mayor Grayson   Judge Grant

The titles of high officials are capitalized even when they are used without the official's name.

the President of the United States   the Secretary of the Treasury
the Governor

Family Relationships. Capitalize the name of a family relationship when it is used with a person's name.

Aunt Helen   Uncle Dave   Cousin Miguel

When words like *mother*, *father*, *dad*, and *mom* are used alone in place of a particular person's name, they are capitalized. When modified by a possessive pronoun, as in *your mother*, they are not capitalized. When these and other words of family relationship do not stand for a particular person, they are not capitalized.

We asked Dad to take us fishing.
Sue's dad will prepare the dinner.

Capitalizing Words Correctly. Supply capital letters where needed in the following sentences.

EXAMPLE: Our family physician is doctor barnes.

1. Do you think your father will be angry with us?
2. The president is flying to europe for a summit conference tomorrow.
3. Did you know that colonel phelps served in the army in korea?
4. The award will be presented by senator coleman.
5. Next week I'll be visiting my aunt helen and uncle joe.
6. Mr. johnson has an appointment to talk with mayor karikomi next week.
7. Cathy has just been promoted to the rank of sergeant.
8. The secretary of the interior watches over federal lands.
9. I wish you could have seen dad's face when he heard the news!
10. Jay's mother shook hands with the governor yesterday.
11. Who served as secretary of state under president carter?
12. Do you know anyone who has had an audience with the pope?
13. Senator-elect jordan will soon give up his law practice.
14. Mr. Stubbens gave captain fleming a ride home from the airport.
15. Who is the present prime minister of britain?
16. I saw aunt cora going into doctor ruben's office.

Titles of Books and Works of Art. Capitalize the first word and every important word in the titles of books, stories, articles, poems, films, works of art, and musical compositions. The only words considered not important are conjunctions, articles (*a*, *an*, and *the*), and prepositions containing fewer than five letters. However, even these are capitalized when used as the first word in a title.

Gone with the Wind   "The Road Not Taken"
The Call of the Wild   "Nobody Knows the Trouble I've Seen"

The Deity. Capitalize all words referring to the Deity, the Holy Family, and to religious scriptures.

God   the Son   the Lord   the Gospel
the Father   the Holy Spirit the Bible   the Talmud

Days, Months, Holidays. Capitalize the names of days of the week, of months, and of holidays. Do not capitalize the names of the seasons.

Thursday   September   Christmas   Thanksgiving   summer   winter

Historical Names. Capitalize the names of historical events, documents, and periods.

World War I   the Declaration of Independence   the Middle Ages

Capitalizing Words Correctly. Supply capital letters where needed.

EXAMPLE: We studied the battle of the bulge in history class.

1. Lewis loves Joan Miró's *still life with old shoe*.

2. We will have a four-day thanksgiving holiday this fall.

3. Does columbus day always fall on monday?

4. The vedas are ancient scriptures of the Indian religion known as hinduism.

5. School will be closed on washington's birthday this year.

6. During the middle ages, castles were built throughout Europe.

7. Sue has three uncles who fought in world war II.

8. The koran is the sacred book of the moslems.

9. Have you read *spoon river anthology*, by edgar lee masters?

10. Brother often fought against brother in the civil war.

11. The first book of the bible is called genesis.

12. We studied the declaration of independence in american history class.

13. The film club discussed *citizen kane* today.

14. Child labor was common during the industrial revolution.

15. Denise Levertov wrote the poem called "a tree telling of orpheus."

16. The bill of rights, the name given to the first ten amendments to the constitution of the United States, guarantees religious freedom.

Supply capital letters where needed in the following sentences.

EXAMPLE: diane moved to northbrook, illinois, in november.

1. we studied the iliad by homer, a greek who lived in about 750 b.c.

2. hamlet said, "to be or not to be, that is the question."

3. has steve read any plays by thornton wilder?

4. brenda hopes to visit concord, massachusetts, the home of emerson and thoreau.

5. stanley karnow's book vietnam: a history was the basis of a television documentary.

6. benjamin franklin said, "half the truth is often a great lie."

7. i watched an interview with geraldine chaplin, daughter of actor charlie chaplin.

8. the goldmans are driving to florida and will cross the smokey mountains.

9. the traffic on crawford avenue is heavy on thursdays and saturdays.

10. french, italian, and spanish all derive from latin.

11. the catalog advertised beautiful english china imported from london.

12. the tour bus crossed the golden gate bridge into marin county.

13. wyatt earp lived in tombstone, arizona, but he died in los angeles, california.

14. the caputos headed south to mount vernon to see george washington's home.

15. holly visited boot hill last year during her trip out west on the amtrak vista dome.

16. the wedding will be held at the beth el synagogue on elmwood and fifth.

17. my grandfather works in the gift shop at st. luke's hospital.

18. my cousin stan attends san leandro high school.

19. reverend adams read from the bible during his sunday sermon.

20. the awards were presented by senator winston wilson.

21. i'm asking mom right now; go ask your dad.

22. last thanksgiving, aunt helen and uncle jerry visited us from scarsdale.

23. in english class, we are reading the poem "ode on a grecian urn" by john keats.

24. olive plans to watch jane eyre on television tonight.

25. during the great depression, many businesses went bankrupt.

26. the bahai temple is a beautiful structure built on the shore of lake michigan.

27. the eighteenth century is often referred to as the age of reason.

28. the hittites were the earliest known inhabitants of the country known today as turkey.

29. patricia harris headed the department of health and human services under president jimmy carter.

30. i didn't know that a belgian is a breed of draft horse.

Periods and Other End Marks

Periods. Place a period at the close of every declarative sentence and of most imperative sentences. A period is also used at the close of groups of words that are used as sentences even though they are not complete sentences.

Please open the window.
I never question your decisions. Never.

Place a period after every part of an abbreviation.

H. G. Wells   Ave.   S. Dak.   P.M.

It has become the custom not to use periods in abbreviations of certain government agencies and international organizations.

FBI   FDA   CIA   NASA   UN

Exclamation Points. Place an exclamation point after an exclamatory sentence and after an exclamation set off from a sentence.

What a sight!   Olson for Governor!   Ouch!   No!

Question Marks. Place a question mark after an interrogative sentence and after a question that is not a complete sentence.

Can you tell me the date?   Do you know?   When?   Where?

Punctuating Sentences. Add periods, question marks, and exclamation points where they are needed in the following sentences.

EXAMPLE: Our delegate to the UN will address the meeting at 10:30 A.M.

1. Dr. Elizabeth Blackwell was the first female physician in the USA.

2. The Ming Period of Chinese history lasted from AD. 1368 to 1644.

3. Don't slam that door!

4. Ms. Hobbs designed the new apartment house at Linden Ave. and Third St.

5. Do you know what W. C. Fields's real name was?

6. You should definitely see a doctor about your cough. Definitely.

7. What a lucky break!

8. Mr. F. R. Cho has been named manager of the Loomis Woolen Mills.

9. W. C. Handy is remembered as the composer of "St Louis Blues".

10. I found out that the UN distributes government publications.

11. Wasn't Barbara C. Jordan in the House of Representatives for six years?

12. What a close call I had.

13. What a relief The neighbors finally turned off their car's burglar alarm!

14. The V.A. administers benefits to veterans and their dependents.

15. Franklin D. Roosevelt took office when our country was in a depression.

Introductory Words. Words such as *yes*, *no*, *well*, *why*, and *oh* are followed by a comma.

No, I can't go today.   Why, I forgot all about it!   Oh, I forgot to tell you.

Introductory Phrases and Clauses. These are followed by a comma.

PARTICIPIAL PHRASE: *Crossing the street*, I stumbled and fell.
ADVERBIAL CLAUSE: *When I became tired*, I lay down for a nap.
A SERIES OF PREPOSITIONAL PHRASES: *At the back of the house*, we planted a garden.

A single prepositional phrase at the beginning of a sentence may be set off by a comma if it is followed by a natural pause when read.

Transposed Words and Phrases. Words and phrases moved to the beginning of the sentence from their normal position are usually set off by a comma.

Obviously, he'd hate to miss his sister's wedding.

Appositives. An appositive is set off by commas.

Our physician, Dr. Grunwald, arrived at ten o'clock.

Using Commas. In the following sentences, insert commas where they belong.

1. Carefully, Irma marked her answers on the test booklet.
2. Why, I never would have recognized you, in those pictures.
3. Marie Curie, a chemist and physicist, was the first person to win two Nobel Prizes.
4. Although Greg is not an experienced cook, he enjoys preparing meals.
5. Oh, were you hurt?
6. Normally, I wouldn't have been upset by David's question.
7. Smiling amiably, Mrs. Olson introduced me, to her husband.
8. Well, I've done about as much as I can do, for one day.
9. When you've finished your revision, proofread your paper carefully.
10. Obviously, I don't want to miss Dan's graduation.
11. As Rob was watching television last night he fell asleep.
12. Rising and stretching Bill began to rub his eyes.
13. No I haven't decided what to do.
14. Mr. Rolf a registered nurse is in charge of first aid at the plant.
15. No Ponce de León never discovered the Fountain of Youth.
16. At the beginning of the season we knew we would have to work hard to win.
17. Although he was only 5'8" tall Pelé was an outstanding soccer player.
18. As Jeanne picked up the paper she saw that someone had scribbled on it.
19. Naturally I'll try to be there for the meeting.
20. At the top of the pear tree at the edge of the orchard a blackbird sat staring at us.

Punctuating Sentences. Add periods, question marks, and exclamation points where they are needed in the following sentences.

EXAMPLE: P. T. Barnum originated a traveling circus.

1. Are crickets and locusts related?

2. At 9:15 A.M. the satellite was launched.

3. Hooray! We've won the debate tournament.

4. The police are directing traffic at Main St. and McCormick Ave.

5. I don't like peanut butter or cheese spreads. Really.

6. Did J. R. R. Tolkien or C. S. Lewis write *The Hobbit*?

7. Are you willing to spend five dollars to see a movie? I'm not.

8. Whew! I just missed getting hit by a fly ball!

9. Did you know that the heart is a muscle?

10. Ms. Dalbok, our librarian, is shelving the new books now.

Using Commas. In the following sentences, insert commas as needed.

EXAMPLE: Carolyn, my violin teacher, studied at Indiana University.

1. Indeed, I have just completed my assignments.

2. Obviously, we could not go in the rain.

3. After a horse is ridden, it needs to be cooled off by walking.

4. Smiling widely, the magician revealed how he had performed the trick.

5. Allison, our newest little cousin was born last week.

6. Usually, I eat a big breakfast every morning.

7. My sandwich was, unfortunately, squashed in my locker.

8. The first presidential mansion was at 1 Cherry Street, New York, New York.

9. There are, I believe, clean towels in the locker room.

10. Either sit near the window, or sit across the aisle.

11. The corn, peas, and carrots were overcooked.

12. I patched the tent, but I didn't find time to repair the air mattresses.

13. The lunch consisted of sloppy joes, French fries, and cole slaw.

14. The carrier delivered the mail, but the sailing magazine did not arrive.

15. For this project we need to consult books, magazines, encyclopedias, newspapers, and almanacs.

16. The killer whale, which is a large dolphin, can reach a weight of ten tons.

The Semicolon

A semicolon is placed between the main clauses of a compound sentence if no conjunction is used.

> Give me the list; I'll check the names. (semicolon in place of *and*)
> Sue will attend the party; she'll be there a little late. (semicolon in place of *but*)

A semicolon is used between main clauses joined by conjunctive adverbs or by phrases like *for example*, *for instance*, *in fact*.

> Leroy is very tall; *in fact*, he's the tallest student in our class.

A semicolon is used between main clauses joined by a conjunction if the clause before the conjunction contains commas.

> We visited San Francisco, Los Angeles, and San Diego; but we wanted to see still more of California.
> The salesperson was friendly, enthusiastic, and persuasive; but Natalie nonetheless decided against buying the coat.

A semicolon is used between a series of phrases if they contain commas.

> We have relatives in Seattle, Washington; Austin, Texas; and Jackson, Mississippi.

Using Semicolons. In the following sentences, replace commas with semicolons wherever necessary.

> **EXAMPLE:** Come visit me when you can,; I'm always glad to see you.

1. I'm exhausted, I've been playing tennis all day.

2. The silkworm is not a worm, in fact, it is a caterpillar.

3. Dave takes math, English, biology, and art, but he didn't sign up for a foreign language this year.

4. The tourists visited Vienna, Austria, Budapest, Hungary, and Munich, Germany.

5. Sally has attended schools in Rhode Island, Virginia, and Illinois, but she likes our school best.

6. My sister Martha won the scholarship, furthermore, she is also eligible for financial aid from the college.

7. A Swedish smorgasbord offers a variety of foods, typical items include pickled herring, salmon, meats, and cheeses.

8. Several members of the Student Council could not attend the meeting, consequently, we had to reschedule it for another time.

9. Mr. Emery is a computer programmer, moreover, he also sells his own software.

10. We added fertilizer to the garden this spring, as a result we had a bumper crop of vegetables.

11. Ada can help in the library every afternoon, however, she cannot work in the evenings.

12. During the 1930's, dust storms destroyed huge areas of farmland, these storms could move faster than fifty miles an hour.

The Colon

A colon is used to introduce a list of items. Often it is preceded by the words *the following*, or *as follows*. The colon is not used before a series of modifiers or complements immediately following the verb.

> We have visited the following countries: Mexico, Panama, Guatemala, and Venezuela.
> The girls in the play were Helen, Nancy, and Betty. (series of complements)

A colon is used to introduce a formal quotation or statement.

> The President began his speech by saying: "We must decide how best to work with our Allies."

A colon is used between two sentences when the second explains the first. The second sentence begins with a capital letter.

> James Jordan smiled happily: He had just been elected Governor.

A colon is also used (1) after the formal salutation of a letter, (2) between hour and minute figures of clock time, (3) in biblical references, (4) between the title and subtitle of a book, (5) between numbers referring to volume and pages of books and magazines.

> Gentlemen: 1:30 P.M.   Exodus 20:3
> *Captain Caution: A Chronicle of Arundel*   Volume III: page 68

Using Colons. Place a colon wherever it is needed below.

1. Our plane leaves at 8 30 A.M. tomorrow.

2. Have you read *The Late George Apley A Novel in the Form of a Memoir*?

3. The following types of sailboats were docked in the harbor sloops, yawls, schooners, and ketches.

4. Wesley found the answer to his question in Volume IV page 38.

5. The minister read from John 20 1-18 this morning.

6. Next fall Rob will select four of the following six subjects French, physics, history, English, humanities, and geometry.

7. The currencies used in Europe include the following francs, escudos, pesetas, lire, and marks.

8. Abigail Adams wrote to John Quincy Adams "Great necessities call out great virtues."

9. To apply for the job you will need to supply the following a summary of the schools you've attended, a list of your previous jobs, and the names of three references.

10. These animal names are from Indian languages woodchuck, chipmunk, and skunk.

11. The following players were honored at the banquet Tim Jacobson, Dan Mendini, and John Lukasa.

12. The mayor ended her speech with a quotation from Aesop "Familiarity breeds contempt."

13. Immediately notify the three understudies Pat, Rudy, and Sol.

14. Take all the equipment we must be prepared for bad weather.

The Dash and Parentheses

A dash is used to show a break or interruption in thought, or after a series to indicate a summarizing statement.

> The botany field trip—demanding but productive—took all morning.
> Necklaces, bracelets, watches, rings—all the jeweler's wares were on display.

Parentheses are used to enclose supplementary or explanatory words. Usually the material enclosed by parentheses is so loosely related to the main thought that it might be better rewritten as a separate sentence.

> Coretta (not Lewis) made the speech on nuclear energy.
> I have a feeling (don't you?) that Norma will get the part in the play.

Using the Dash and Parentheses. Add the necessary punctuation to these sentences, following the directions given in parentheses.

> EXAMPLE: I knew you—with your interest in astronomy—would find the planetarium show intriguing.

1. Pumpkin seeds and sunflower seeds you can roast them yourself are surprisingly delicious. (Add dashes.)

2. Juanita's gymnastic routine a dazzling performance was my favorite part of the program. (Add dashes.)

3. Sightseeing, meeting new people, eating different foods all this was over much too quickly. (Add a dash.)

4. I'm sure aren't you? that Marcia will get the job. (Add parentheses.)

5. Building your own canoe an exacting and exhausting job can give great satisfaction. (Add dashes.)

6. Skim milk to which I am allergic is on Debra's diet. (Add parentheses.)

7. Books, radio, television, crossword puzzles all these kept Tom busy while he was in the hospital. (Add dash.)

8. The election campaign more details later took all our energy. (Add parentheses.)

9. I have relatives living in several southern states Alabama, Georgia, Mississippi, and Virginia. (Add a dash.)

10. After I had my tonsils out, milk shakes not solid food tasted good to me. (Add parentheses.)

11. The students not the faculty advisor chose the band for the dance. (Add parentheses.)

12. Ellie can't participate in some of her favorite activities skiing, jogging, ice skating because of her recent back injury. (Add dashes.)

13. Amber the fossilized resin of certain evergreens was once thought to have healing properties. (Add dashes.)

14. A huge flock of gulls the largest flock I've ever seen landed on the beach just beyond the sand dunes. (Add dashes.)

15. Our old car affectionately known as "The Blue Blob" still runs well in all kinds of weather, despite our worst fears. (Add parentheses.)

Review: The Semicolon, Colon, Dash, and Parentheses

Using Semicolons. In the following sentences, replace a comma with a semicolon wherever a semicolon is needed.

    EXAMPLE: Seven people climbed the Matterhorn in 1865,;four of them died on the treacherous descent.

1. Koumiss is made from mare's milk, it is a popular beverage in Russia.
2. I enjoy reading mysteries, for instance, I love Agatha Christie's novels.
3. The contestants came from Chicago, Illinois, Milwaukee, Wisconsin, and San Francisco, California.
4. We dusted, scrubbed, mopped, and swept, but still the cabin looked a mess.
5. The days are getting shorter, soon unfortunately it will be winter.
6. Connie is moving in June. We should give her a surprise party.

Using the Colon. Place a colon where it belongs in each sentence below.

    EXAMPLE: The American linden is also known by the following names lime tree, linn, and basswood.

1. The visiting schedule is as follows parents on Monday, friends on Tuesday.
2. The job has three requirements punctuality, speed, and accuracy.
3. The situation is clear All the bikes must be put in the garage.
4. The teacher recommended two writers Willa Cather and Eudora Welty.
5. The bus leaves at 12 30 and every half hour thereafter.
6. Follow the instructions always use the buddy system.

Using the Dash and Parentheses. In the following sentences, insert dashes or parentheses where they are needed.

    EXAMPLE: The field trip more interesting than we had expected lasted all day.

1. Charles Lindbergh named "Lucky Lindy" by the press began his aviation career performing daredevil stunts at fairs. (Add parentheses.)
2. The director not the actors came out to take a bow after the play. (Add parentheses.)
3. Fatty foods not fruits and vegetables contribute to high cholesterol. (Add dashes.)
4. The marigolds, the zinnias, the sweet peas all were in bloom. (Add dash.)
5. All of her experience she lived in Mexico for two years becomes material for her short stories. (Add parentheses.)
6. A hurricane the third this season battered the coast. (Add dashes.)

The Possessive of Nouns (I)

The **apostrophe** is used with nouns to show possession or ownership. The possessive form of a singular noun is usually made by adding an apostrophe and *s* (*'s*).

Don—Don's dog   girl—girl's bicycle

The possessive of plural nouns is formed by adding an apostrophe and *s* (*'s*). However, if the plural noun ends in *s*, add only the apostrophe to form the possessive.

children—children's toys   birds—birds' cages
salesperson—salesperson's ideas   books—books' covers

Using Apostrophes Correctly. For each of the following sentences, write the correct possessive form of the italicized noun.

EXAMPLE: The four *witnesses* testimony differed substantially. _____*witnesses'*_____

1. The *tourist* accounts of their trip were all different. ___tourist's___

2. The *Roosevelts* summer home was on Campobello Island. ___Roosevelts'___

3. His *wife* sister is my neighbor. ___wife's___

4. The *gallery* collection of Eskimo art is marvelous. ___gallery's___

5. The *debaters* meeting will be held at four o'clock. ___debaters'___

6. The *men* shoes in that store are all imported from Italy. ___men's___

7. Local journalists are attending an *editors* conference in Des Moines. ___editors'___

8. The *cities* advantages include excellent public transportation systems. ___cities'___

9. The *toys* safety features are an important selling point. ___toys'___

10. The *sopranos* duet was well received. ___sopranos'___

11. The *landscaper* ideas are being considered by the architect. ___landscaper's___

12. The *children* playground includes modern climbing equipment. ___children's___

13. *Lapland* winter lasts nine months. _____

14. My *sister* house key has disappeared. _____

15. Haven't the *actors* parts been difficult to learn? _____

16. The returning astronaut received a *hero* welcome. _____

17. The *judge* decision stunned the courtroom. _____

18. *Jane* hobby is knitting sweaters from wool she has spun herself. _____

19. The *waiter* tips for the day amounted to a large sum. _____

20. James inspected all the *animals* cages at the zoo. _____

The Possessive of Nouns (II)

A **compound noun** is a noun composed of more than one word. Only the last part of a compound noun shows possession.

   father-in-law's car   editor-in-chief's job

When two or more nouns are used to show joint ownership, only the last noun mentioned is given the possessive form. The rule also applies to firm names and to names of organizations.

   Susan and Brad's church   National Food Store's policy

If the nouns are used to show separate ownership, each name is given the possessive form.

   Helen's and Margaret's houses   Jack's and Ken's jackets

Use an apostrophe and *s* to form the possessive of indefinite pronouns: *one's* boat, *someone else's* house. Never use an apostrophe to form the possessive of personal pronouns: *ours, yours, his, hers, its, theirs.*

Using Apostrophes Correctly. For the following sentences, write the correct possessive form of the italicized words. If the sentence is correct as it is, write *Correct* in the blank.

  EXAMPLE: The *robins* and *sparrows* nests were empty. _robins' sparrows'_

1. The driver stopped the taxi in front of *Ellen* and *Mary* school. _E. & Mary's_

2. The schnauzer is wagging *its* tail. _its_

3. Isn't that navy blue jacket *yours*? _yours_

4. Ben shoveled the snow off his *brother-in-law* driveway. _b.-i-law's_

5. That must be *someone else* dirt bike. _someone else's_

6. *Ellie* and *Rudy* names appeared in the credits after the movie. _E. & Rudy's_

7. What are the *National Music Camp* requirements for admission? _N. M. Camp's_

8. Our poor harvest from the vegetable garden is *nobody* fault. _nobody's_

9. The Whitmans turned in their tickets, but we gave away *ours*. _ours_

10. The *Morgans* and *Swansons* cars were damaged in the collision. _Morgan's and Swanson's_

11. The *sergeant-at-arms* attention was distracted by the singing in the hallway. _____

12. I always wash my sweaters, but Jill has *hers* dry-cleaned. _____

13. *Nobody* swimming form is perfect. _____

14. *Jack* cat never goes outdoors. _____

15. What are the *editor-in-chief* duties? _____

16. Have you been to *Jordan and Jackson* sale? _____

Other Uses of the Apostrophe

When used as adjectives, words expressing time and amount are possessive.

   an hour's pay   three months' wait   two months' work

An apostrophe is used to show the omission of letters or figures.

   class of '81 (1981)   couldn't (could not)   we're (we are)

An apostrophe is also used to show the plurals of letters, words, numbers, and signs. (In print, such expressions are *italicized*. In manuscript, they may be underlined or placed in quotation marks.)

   How many *s's* are in your name?
   He used too many *if's* in his talk.
   Saddle shoes were popular in the 1940's.

Using Apostrophes Correctly. Write the correct possessive or plural form of the italicized word in each sentence below.

   EXAMPLE: I lost a *day* practice when I was sick. _____ *day's* _____

1. There will be three *months* delay in the construction of the building. __months'__

2. Eleven *oclock* in England is known as elevenses, time for a tea break. __o'clock__

3. Manny lost points on the math test; all his *2s* looked like *3s*. __2's__ __3's__

4. Ms. Woods graduated from college with the class of *81*. __'81__

5. *Wasnt* basketball originally played with a peach basket instead of a net? __Wasn't__

6. Jim bought five *dollars* worth of snacks last night. __dollars'__

7. In 1889 Nellie Bly, age 22, traveled around the world in seventy-two *days* time. __days'__

8. Be sure you dot your *is* in your papers. __i's__

9. The Wilson family had gone to the World's Fair of *84*. __'84__

10. *Were* always eager to listen to new ideas. __We're__

11. Seven *years* study is needed to become a lawyer. _____

12. Rachels house is just ten *minutes* walk from mine. _____

13. You *mustnt* worry about things beyond your control. _____

14. Mike said thirteen *ums* during his speech. _____

15. *Well* be in the city in one hour. _____

16. The past *year* history has been full of political surprises. _____

17. Five *cents* worth of bread was probably a lot in 1900. _____

18. The use of videos and computers has skyrocketed in the *1980s*. _____

Review: The Apostrophe

Using Apostrophes Correctly. For each of the following sentences, write the correct possessive form of the italicized noun.

EXAMPLE: The *dignitaries* seats were all reserved. _____ *dignitaries'* _____

1. The *farmer* fields were flooded for a week. _____ *farmer's* _____

2. Dr. Seuss has written many popular *children* books. _____ *children's* _____

3. The *men* locker room is overcrowded. _____ *men's* _____

4. The *playwright* works are usually performed without scenery. _____ *playwright's* _____

5. The weeping *willow* roots were interfering with the sewer. _____ *willow's* _____

6. The *counselors* cabins are near the lake. _____ *counselors'* _____

7. It is the *editor-in-chief* job to decide what articles will be printed. _____ *-in-chief's* _____

8. Have you ever met *Bonnie and Allen* parents? _____ *Bonnie's & Allen's* _____

9. We recommended that they buy a lawn mower like *ours*. _____ *ours* _____

10. *No ones* suggestion will be ignored. _____ *No one's* _____

11. The teacher was impressed with *David* and *Matt* work. _____

12. Maria likes to buy that *dairy* milk because it is fresh daily. _____

13. The Hundred *Years* War actually lasted for 116 years. _____

14. We responded to *Lancomb and Stevens* ad for help wanted. _____

Using Apostrophes Correctly. Rewrite each of the following sentences. Insert apostrophes where needed.

EXAMPLE: The little boy could not say his *ss*.

_____ *The little boy could not say his s's* _____

1. Beginning readers often confuse *bs*, *ds*, *ps*, and *qs*.

_____

2. Barbara couldnt follow his argument because of all the *ifs*, *ands*, and *buts*.

_____

3. In two weeks time the class of 88 had raised enough money for a new computer.

_____

4. The 30s were difficult years for the American people.

_____

Direct Quotations

Quotation marks are used to enclose a *direct quotation*. In a direct quotation, the words of the speaker are directly quoted exactly as spoken.

Quotation marks are never used with an indirect quotation, which reports the meaning of the speaker but not the exact words.

> **INDIRECT:** Lionel said that he would like to play tennis.
> **DIRECT:** Lionel said, "I would like to play tennis."
>
> **INDIRECT:** The woman asked Dave if he needed a job.
> **DIRECT:** "Do you need a job?" the woman asked Dave.

Identifying Direct Quotations. Read each sentence below. If it is a direct quotation and requires quotation marks, write **D** in the blank. If the sentence is an indirect quotation, write **I** in the blank.

EXAMPLE: I bought a new chess set, said Mary. _____D_____

1. Alice said sadly, I hope we can see one another during summer vacation. _____D_____

2. The teacher asked us to be quiet. _____I_____

3. I will introduce the speaker, said Adam. _____D_____

4. Thoreau said that some people march to a different drummer. _____I_____

5. Ms. Keith asked, Do you think summer will ever come? _____D_____

6. The teacher asked if we understood the journal writing assignment. _____I_____

7. Do you want to go to the movies? asked Ken. _____D_____

8. Edna St. Vincent Millay wrote, Time can make soft that iron wood. _____D_____

9. Sonia said that she had already studied her French assignment. _____I_____

10. Zachary asked why no one had given him a surprise party. _____I_____

11. Five weeks is too long to live out of a suitcase, the girl replied. _____

12. The policewoman asked if we had seen anyone wearing a red sweatshirt. _____

13. I've never played backgammon before, admitted George. _____

14. Don't count your chickens before they are hatched, warned Aesop. _____

15. What is your favorite novel? asked Susan. _____

16. Ms. Turner said that we should note which trees were deciduous and which were evergreens. _____

17. The only thing we have to fear is fear itself, said President Roosevelt. _____

18. The reports of my death are greatly exaggerated, quipped Mark Twain after a newspaper mistakenly declared him dead. _____

Writing Direct Quotations

In dialogue, the first word of the quotation is capitalized. The speaker's words are set off from the rest of the sentence by a comma. When the end of the quotation is also the end of the sentence, the end punctuation falls inside the quotation marks.

> Marian said, "I've seen that movie three times."

If the quoted words are a question or exclamation, the end punctuation falls inside the quotation marks unless the whole sentence is a question or exclamation.

> "Ouch! I burned my finger!" Susan cried.
> Did Bob say, "It's my fault"?

Material quoted may begin in the middle of a sentence; if so, the first word is not capitalized. At the close of a quotation, a colon or semicolon falls outside the quotation marks.

> Mary said that people "can live graciously only in the South"; I don't agree.

Both parts of a divided quotation are enclosed in quotes, but the second part is not capitalized unless it is a new sentence. A new paragraph and new quotation marks show a change in speaker.

> "The mayor's speech was wonderful," said Ms. Brown. "I enjoyed it."
> "But," said her husband, "hadn't you heard it all before?"

Writing Quotations Correctly. Read each sentence below. Insert the proper punctuation.

EXAMPLE: "What time did you get up this morning?" asked Tim.

1. "What are the working conditions here," asked the reporter at the factory.

2. "I've never known," said Mr. Olivera, "just how to take his comments."

3. "You can't be serious," exclaimed Kate.

4. "Ask not what your country can do for you," said President Kennedy.

5. "We hold these truths to be self-evident," says the *Declaration of Independence*.

6. "I'll take the blame for that," Dan said.

7. "I don't believe a word of it," shouted Ken.

8. "The whole secret of the study of nature," wrote George Sand, "lies in learning how to use one's eyes."

9. Bob admitted, "I don't really understand that problem."

10. "I don't know what I'd do," said Mr. Calini, "without my calculator."

11. Let's play cribbage Kim suggested it's such a good game.

12. I will not stay late again announced Pat.

13. Would you like to play some racquetball asked Mother.

14. I'm sure said Tina that I should be saving more money.

15. Did Rick say it's too hot to play tennis?

Copyright © 1985 by McDougal, Littell & Company

More About Quotations

Quotations within Quotations. Single quotation marks are used to enclose a quotation within a quotation.

> "The sign says, 'Deposit all litter in trash barrel,' " Dad mentioned.
> Tom said, "I'm glad Rosa told me, 'I agree completely.' "

Setting Off Titles. Use quotation marks to enclose the titles of chapters, stories, poems, essays, articles, and songs.

> You'd like James Plunkett's short story "The Half-Crown."
> "Youth and Age" is a poem by the Irish writer, Eleanor Hull.

Words Used in Special Ways. Words used in special ways are enclosed in quotation marks.

> Ben calls the people of our town the "locals."

A word referred to as a word is put in italics.

> The word *ingress* means "entrance."

Using Quotations Correctly. Insert the appropriate punctuation in each of the following sentences.

> **EXAMPLE:** "The Boy Scouts' motto is 'Be prepared,' " said Dave.

1. Have you read O. Henry's short story The Whirligig of Life?
2. Jim told me You and I will never get rich said Martha.
3. The word *dollop* means a lump or a large hunk.
4. I know you'd like Robert Frost's poem Birches.
5. Didn't the restaurant's ad say Open at Five O'clock Tracy asked.
6. Have you ever read Dorothy Parker's poem Surprise?
7. What's wrong with saying Between you and me asked Gina.
8. Do you know the song Country Roads asked Vicki.
9. The instructions say Wash in hot water Pete explained.
10. Al said I like to read novels by Rex Stout answered Melva.
11. To Build a Fire is the name of a good short story by Jack London.
12. Al asked Are you sure that Todd said That's not my job
13. I dislike the expression Have a good day.
14. There are several stories I'd recommend, such as Lilacs.
15. In the book *The Asians* I was especially interested in the chapter The Japanese Woman and the chapter Politics in Japan.
16. Let me read you Ogden Nash's poem Kind of an Ode to Duty.
17. Didn't the sign say Newton—10 Miles asked Mother.
18. Can you say she sells seashells down by the seashore?

Review: Quotations

Identifying Direct Quotations. Read each sentence below. If it is a direct quotation and requires quotation marks, write **D** in the blank. If the sentence is an indirect quotation, write **I** in the blank.

> **EXAMPLE:**   There's a fly in my soup, complained the patron. _____

1.   Jerry said he was tired and wanted to rest. _____

2.   Help yourself to the fruit, said Mother. _____

3.   We asked the neighbors to take in our mail during our vacation. _____

4.   Follow that car! the man shouted, jumping into a cab. _____

5.   When the announcer says, And now time out for a station break, that's my cue to

make a sandwich. _____

Writing Quotations Correctly. Read each sentence below. Insert the proper punctuation where needed.

> **EXAMPLE:**   Gail asked,"How can you eat strawberries without cream?"

1.   Wow! said the little boy, I have never seen so many sailboats.

2.   You should act now, said the salesperson, before the price goes up.

3.   The dictionary said that lapis lazuli is a blue precious stone.

4.   I wonder how much it costs to rent a horse and carriage, said Jolene.

5.   Did Malcolm really say, I can't come tomorrow? asked Cecilia.

6.   The veterinarian asked, When did your cat stop eating normally?

7.   Somehow, pondered the deliveryman, I have to get this refrigerator up three flights of stairs and through that narrow doorway.

8.   The clock must have stopped, observed Camilla. Do you know what time it is?

9.   Watch out, warned the foreman. This is a hard-hat area!

10.   Who is responsible for this accident? questioned the policeman.

Using Quotations Correctly. Insert the appropriate punctuation in each of the following sentences.

> **EXAMPLE:**   The social worker said,"This report is marked 'Confidential.'"

1.   The word *egress* means exit.

2.   The sign warns No Trespassing, exclaimed Valerie to her friends.

3.   I like the poem Annabel Lee by Edgar Allan Poe, said Caroline.

4.   Why did Dad say Get to bed? wondered Carlos.

5.   Charles Dickens wrote the line It was the best of times; it was the worst of times.

The Final Silent e

When a suffix beginning with a vowel is added to a word ending in a silent *e*, the *e* is usually dropped.

    take—taking   admire—admiration
    fame—famous   fascinate—fascination

When the final silent *e* is preceded by *c* or *g*, the *e* is usually retained before a suffix beginning with *a* or *o*.

    notice—noticeable   manage—manageable

When a suffix beginning with a consonant is added to a word ending in silent *e*, the *e* is usually retained.

    same—sameness   improve—improvement
    EXCEPTIONS   truly, argument, wholly, awful

Adding Suffixes to Words Ending in Silent e. In each sentence below, change the italicized word to the correct form. Choose from these suffixes: *-ing, -al, -ion, -ation, -able, -ous, -ful, -less, -ly, -ment.*

    EXAMPLE: The boys gave an *amaze* performance on the trampoline. *amazing*

1. Mr. Morgan has many *admire* qualities. _____

2. Did you have an *appraise* of the value of your house? _____

3. Tony is *grease* the pan before he makes the applesauce cake. _____

4. Today's discussion is a *continue* of yesterday's. _____

5. The Jacksons are thinking of *name* the baby Sabra. _____

6. Dick Mason found himself *fame* overnight. _____

7. Harriet Tubman had no opportunity for formal *educate*. _____

8. Whether Jack should take that job is *debate*. _____

9. American society has been *change* rapidly since 1900. _____

10. A rhinocerous is unpredictable and *danger*. _____

11. To Beth's *amaze*, she won first prize for her essay. _____

12. Coyotes roam *wide* throughout the Northwest Territory. _____

13. When I get tired, I make *care* mistakes. _____

14. I have much *admire* for long distance runners. _____

15. Have you studied the *Constitute* of the United States? _____

16. Louise will be *live* in France next year. _____

Words Ending in y

When a suffix is added to a word ending in *y* preceded by a consonant, the *y* is usually changed to *i*.

There are two exceptions: (1) when *-ing* is added, the *y* does not change; (2) some one-syllable words do not change the *y*, as *dryness*, *shyness*.

hazy—haziness	envy—envying
cherry—cherries	penny—pennies
marry—married	merry—merriment

When a suffix is added to a word ending in *y* preceded by a vowel, the *y* usually does not change.

say—saying	employ—employer
joy—joyful	delay—delayed

EXCEPTIONS daily, gaily

Adding Suffixes to Words Ending in y. In each sentence below, change the italicized word to the correct form. Choose from these suffixes: *-ness, -es, -ed, -age, -ing, -able, -er, -ful, -est, -ly.*

EXAMPLE: Tandra and Darrel were *marry* in June. _married_____

1. The children watched the *play* lambs. _____

2. The networks are *relay* the coronation via satellite. _____

3. The aviator's homecoming was a *joy* occasion. _____

4. Ed reads the *funny* before anything else in the paper. _____

5. The Romans *carry* their culture to all parts of their empire. _____

6. The *dry* of the soil is a serious problem. _____

7. The little boy bought a unicorn sticker with his five *penny*. _____

8. Tutankhamen was *bury* with a vast treasure. _____

9. The sky is *gray* over the lake. _____

10. The defense attorney questioned the *fair* of the trial. _____

11. We will be *buy* a bushel of apples at the farm. _____

12. That is the *cheery* song I know. _____

13. Dr. Owens went on her *day* rounds as if nothing had happened. _____

14. As a young man, Richard Wright was *employ* at the post office. _____

15. The geese ran about the barnyard, squawking *noisy*. _____

16. We *enjoy* our visit to the world's fair. _____

Prefixes and Suffixes

The Suffixes -*ness* and -*ly*. When the suffix -*ly* is added to a word ending in *l*, both *l*'s are retained. When -*ness* is added to a word ending in *n*, both *n*'s are retained.

actual—actually   even—evenness
gradual—gradually   thin—thinness

The Addition of Prefixes. When a prefix is added to a word, the spelling of the word remains the same.

*dis*appear   *pre*soak   *trans*action   *mis*step
*im*prove   *re*zone   *co*operate   *ir*relevant

Words with the "Seed" Sound. Only one English word ends in *sede*: *supersede*. Three other words end in *ceed*: *exceed, proceed, succeed*. All other words ending in the "seed" sound are spelled *cede*: *secede, recede, concede, accede, precede*.

Correcting Spelling Errors. Underline the spelling error in each of the following sentences. Write the correct spelling of each underlined word in the blank.

EXAMPLE: We gradualy increased our speed. _____ *gradually*

1. The panda bear actualy is not a bear at all. _____

2. When did South Carolina sesede from the Union? _____

3. The eveness of the two teams made the game exciting to watch. _____

4. The candidate conseded defeat with graciousness and dignity. _____

5. The thiness of the ice made skating dangerous. _____

6. The doctor carefuly examined Jody's broken arm. _____

7. New methods of recording sound have superceded old ones. _____

8. The flood waters have finally begun to receed. _____

9. The great cathedrals were built gradualy over several centuries. _____

10. Ostrich eggs are substantialy larger than those of other birds. _____

11. Everyone is dressing casualy for the party. _____

12. Does Iowa's production of corn excede Ohio's? _____

13. The cellist acceeded to the audience's pleas for an encore. _____

14. We appreciated Mr. Montega's openess and flexibility. _____

15. After twenty years Ulysses suceeded in returning home. _____

16. The dignitaries slowly proceded to the platform. _____

17. Ms. Ruiz preceeded us into the auditorium. _____

18. Did the conductor on the train speak to you civily? _____

Words with *ie* and *ei*

When the sound is long *e* (ē), the word is spelled *ie* except after *c*.

I BEFORE E

piece   priest   brief   yield   chief

EXCEPT AFTER C

perceive   ceiling   conceive   deceit   receipt

EXCEPTIONS TO THE RULE

either   neither   financier   weird   species   seize   leisure

Correcting Spelling Errors. Underline the misspelled word in each sentence below. Write the word correctly in the blank.

EXAMPLE: What is your <u>beleif</u> about the treaty?   _____*belief*_____

1. Can iether the kiwi or the emu fly?   _____

2. Mr. Todd raises orchids in his liesure time.   _____

3. The cieling of the Sistine Chapel is one of Michelangelo's masterpieces.   _____

4. Breifly, here are my plans for the week.   _____

5. Nancy would not yeild her point despite our arguments.   _____

6. Mrs. Hansen's neice is learning how to train dolphins.   _____

7. Without her reciept, Fran was unable to return the shoes.   _____

8. A peice of cloth was the detective's only clue.   _____

9. He was quick to percieve the child's feelings.   _____

10. Her aim is not simply to weild power.   _____

11. Geronimo was a famous Chiricohua Apache cheif.   _____

12. Niether Peter nor Ted knows how to play chess.   _____

13. The child is greiving over the death of his hamster.   _____

14. His message was full of trickery and deciet.   _____

15. The financeir is used to dealing with huge sums of money.   _____

16. Sieze every opportunity to improve yourself!   _____

17. What speceis of moth is that?   _____

18. The children dressed in wierd costumes on Halloween.   _____

Doubling the Final Consonant

In words of one syllable ending in one consonant preceded by one vowel, double the final consonant before adding a suffix beginning with a vowel.

sit—sitting   slug—slugged   plan—planning
brag—bragged   big—biggest   tan—tanner

The final consonant is doubled in a word of more than one syllable when the word ends in one consonant preceded by one vowel *and* the word is accented on the last syllable.

omit'—omitted   refer'—referred
submit'—submitted   begin'—beginning

However, if the word is accented on another syllable, the final consonant is not doubled.

confer'—conference   refer'—reference

Correcting Spelling Errors. Underline the misspelled word in each sentence below. Write the word correctly in the blank.

    EXAMPLE: I <u>omited</u> my signature on the letter. _____*omitted*_____

1. Walter had been siting in the dentist's office for an hour. _____

2. What is your preferrence in television programs? _____

3. King Kong's name was omited from the cast of characters. _____

4. We were all runing as fast as we could. _____

5. I've checked every referrence book in the library! _____

6. Are African elephants biger than Asian elephants? _____

7. The whole house smelled like vinegar when we were caning pickles. _____

8. Mrs. Miller is a member of the planing commission. _____

9. Sally submited her letter of resignation to the Student Council. _____

10. When Ned was in Europe, he prefered Italy to France. _____

11. What's the diferrence between the AM and FM bands on the radio? _____

12. Don braged about winning the dance contest. _____

13. Mr. Hunter is a beginer in his yoga class. _____

14. How much of your salary have you alloted to rent? _____

15. The rest of the group is defering to your judgment. _____

16. You are forgeting that you owe me a letter! _____

17. The kitten fliped out of my arms, but walked away unhurt. _____

18. The travelers debated whether Miami was hoter than Honolulu. _____

Words Often Confused (I)

Homonyms are words that sound alike but that are spelled differently and have different meanings. For example, the words *hear*, meaning "to listen to," and *here*, meaning "at this place", are homonyms. Study the following list of homonyms and other words often confused.

capital means excellent, most serious, or most important.
capitol is a building in which a state legislature meets.
the **Capitol** is the building in Washington, D. C., in which the United States Congress meets.
desert means a wilderness or dry sandy region with sparse vegetation.
desert means to abandon.
dessert (note the change in spelling) is a sweet such as cake or pie.
hear means to listen to, or take notice of.
here means in this place.
lose means to mislay or suffer the loss of something.
loose means free or not fastened.

Choosing the Correct Spelling. In each sentence below, underline the correct spelling of the word that properly belongs in the sentence.

EXAMPLE: The sands of the (<u>desert</u>, dessert) are constantly shifting.

1. Your idea is simply (capital, capitol, Capitol)!

2. The cactus is ideally suited to a (desert, dessert) environment.

3. A button on my jacket came (lose, loose).

4. (Hear, Here) is a painting of sunflowers by Vincent Van Gogh.

5. Does the House of Representatives meet in the (capital, capitol, Capitol)?

6. The mother bear will never (desert, dessert) her cubs.

7. Did you (hear, here) the announcement over the loudspeaker?

8. A toga was a (lose, loose), one-piece garment worn in ancient Rome.

9. Our state (capital, capitol, Capitol) building was recently remodeled.

10. Sweet potato pie is Tyrell's favorite (desert, dessert).

11. The seat of my little brother's tricycle is (lose, loose).

12. That puppy must stay right (hear, here) in the kitchen.

13. Don't (lose, loose) your notebook.

14. Did you (hear, here) the doorbell?

15. "You win some, and you (lose, loose) some," muttered Gail after the match.

16. Have you seen the state (capital, capitol, Capitol) in Des Moines?

17. I'm sure Chuck's friends will never (desert, dessert) him.

18. The handle on the doorknob is (lose, loose).

19. (Hear, Here) are the instructions to follow for the scavenger hunt.

20. Citizens were warned to be on the lookout for a (lose, loose) tiger.

Words Often Confused (II)

Here is another list of words often confused.

its is a word that indicates ownership.
it's is a contraction for *it is* or *it has*.
principal describes something or someone of chief or central importance.
principle is a basic truth, standard, or rule of behavior.
stationary means fixed or unmoving.
stationery refers to paper and envelopes used for writing letters.
there means in that place.
their means belonging to them.
they're is a contraction for *they are*.
to means toward, or in the direction of.
too means also or very.
two is the number 2.
weather refers to atmospheric conditions such as temperature or cloudiness.
whether helps express choice or alternative.
whose is the possessive form of who.
who's is a contraction for *who is* or *who has*.
your is the possessive form of *you*.
you're is a contraction for *you are*.

Choosing the Correct Spelling. In each sentence below, underline the correct spelling of the word that properly belongs in the sentence.

1. Breadfruit derives (its, it's) name from the flavor it has when baked.

2. (Whose, Who's) singing the part of Eliza in your production of *My Fair Lady*?

3. What sign does a sailor observe to predict the (weather, whether)?

4. The (principal, principle) of our school is Ms. Lynetta Holmes.

5. Victor learned the (principals, principles) of chess two years ago.

6. Lynn uses a (stationary, stationery) bicycle for exercise in bad weather.

7. Harare is the (principal, principle) city in Zimbabwe, a country in Africa.

8. (Its, It's) never too late to make an apology or renew a friendship.

9. It's not the money; it's the (principal, principle) of the thing!

10. You must make your own decision; (its, it's) completely up to you.

11. Because of (its, it's) lack of gravity, the moon has no atmosphere.

12. Sue doesn't know (weather, whether) to take French, Spanish, or German.

13. Have you ordered (your, you're) dinner yet?

14. (There, Their, They're) ready to take the yearbook photos now.

15. What is the (principal, principle) lesson you've learned from all this?

16. The Wilmores have sold (there, their, they're) house.

17. Angela enjoys writing on different kinds of (stationary, stationery).

18. Is that (your, you're) newest album?

Review: Spelling

Spelling Words with Added Suffixes. In each sentence below, change the italicized word to the correct form by adding a suffix. Choose from these suffixes: *-ing, -al, -ion, -able, -ous, -ful, -less, -ly, -ation, -ness, -es, -ed, -age, -ing, -able, -er, -ful, -ment.*

   EXAMPLE: John is the most *boast* boy in class.   _____boastful_____

1. The doctor was pleased at the *improve* in her patient's condition.   _____

2. My brother is looking forward to his *graduate*.   _____

3. Dad is going into *retire* at the end of the year.   _____

4. How much are they *charge* for those wheel covers?   _____

5. Inez is *hope* to become a veterinarian.   _____

6. We wanted to share our *happy* with our friends.   _____

7. We were *delay* on the runway for almost two hours.   _____

8. The child picked all the *blueberry* out of the muffin.   _____

9. Why are you *hurry* if class doesn't start for ten minutes?   _____

10. We worked *busy* late into the night.   _____

Correcting Spelling Errors. Underline the spelling error in each of the following sentences. Write the correct spelling of each underlined word on the blank.

   EXAMPLE: We took turns carring the canoe.   _____carrying_____

1. The police are investigating these mysterious occurences.   _____

2. I am celebrateing my birthday today.   _____

3. David is actualy five days older than I am.   _____

4. How could you mispell such a simple word?   _____

5. Millions watched the marryage ceremony of Charles and Diana.   _____

6. It was iresponsible of the bus driver to turn like that.   _____

7. Our problem is largly one of lack of enthusiasm.   _____

8. I have not recieved the magazine I subscribed to.   _____

9. What a releif that the temperature is down!   _____

10. Katie is planing to learn origami, the Japanese art of paper folding.   _____

11. The photography at the begining of this movie is breathtaking.   _____

12. The carpenters left there tools on the construction site.   _____

Plurals Formed with *s* and *es*

The plural of most nouns is formed by adding -*s*. The plural of nouns ending in *s*, *sh*, *ch*, *x*, and *z* is formed by adding -*es*.

    cat—cats   brush—brushes

Spelling Plurals Correctly. In each of the following sentences, change the singular noun given in parentheses into the plural form. Write it in the blank.

    EXAMPLE: There are many beautiful (church) in Columbus, Indiana. ___*churches*___

1. How many (employee) does the federal government have? _____

2. Colonial homes had shutters on all the (window). _____

3. Botony and zoology are (branch) of biology. _____

4. Weddings in earlier times often lasted for several (day). _____

5. The students' (badge) bore their names. _____

6. We had five (test) in history last term. _____

7. The ranger showed us the trail of the (fox). _____

8. Our tennis ball vanished somewhere inside the (bush). _____

9. Camel's-hair (brush) are actually made from squirrel's hair. _____

10. How many (bus) go to Burlington each day? _____

11. Before the discovery of metal, (ax) were made from stone. _____

12. Uncle Martin and Aunt Peg exchanged (kiss). _____

13. A cat's (sense) of sight and hearing are especially keen. _____

14. The two (woodchuck) scurried into the underbrush. _____

15. Golda Meir and Elie Wiesel both worked as (teacher). _____

16. Please fill the cardboard (box) with the discarded toys. _____

17. The two most common (gas) are oxygen and nitrogen. _____

18. Many folk tales involve the granting of (wish). _____

19. The students painted three (house) this past summer. _____

20. Sam and Barb packed (lunch) for the picnic. _____

21. Hearing (loss) can be traced to excessively loud music or noise. _____

22. A polyglot is a person who can speak several (language). _____

Nouns Ending in y

When a noun ends in *y* preceded by a consonant, the plural is formed by changing *y* to *i* and adding *-es*.

    company—companies   worry—worries   beauty—beauties

When a noun ends in *y* preceded by a vowel, the plural is formed by adding *-s*.

    play—plays   valley—valleys   delay—delays

Spelling Plurals Correctly. In each of the following sentences, change the singular noun given in parentheses into the plural form. Write it in the blank.

    EXAMPLE: Ann has appeared in three (play) this year. _____*plays*_____

1. The railroad strike caused (delay) in the shipments of food across the nation. _____

2. Those wooden (toy) were all imported from Germany. _____

3. In Russia those writers are considered (enemy) of the state. _____

4. Dan has few (worry) when it comes to making the team. _____

5. (Cherry) are a source of Vitamin A. _____

6. The (boy) in the kindergarten class outnumbered the girls. _____

7. What steel (company) were established in the '20's? _____

8. The new colts were little (beauty). _____

9. Several of the midwestern states have few hills or (valley). _____

10. How many (holiday) are there between New Year's Day and the Fourth of July? _____

11. There are twelve (caddy) on duty at Twin Oaks Golf Course. _____

12. The (boy) raced one another across the field. _____

13. The restaurant roasted five (turkey) for Thanksgiving dinner. _____

14. Old ornate (key) are collector's items today. _____

15. Shakespeare's (play) were performed at the Globe theater. _____

16. The (monkey) in the zoo like to show off for visitors. _____

17. Most major (city) are located near large bodies of water. _____

18. One of his many (folly) was swimming during an electrical storm. _____

19. The waiters' (tray) were heaped high with food. _____

20. The (cry) of the baby were heard outside the window. _____

Nouns Ending in *o*

The plural of nouns ending in *o*, preceded by a vowel, is formed by adding *s*.

cameo—cameos   folio—folios   studio—studios   Eskimo—Eskimos

The plural of most nouns ending in *o*, preceded by a consonant, is formed by adding *s*, but for some nouns of this class the plural is formed by adding *es*.

piano—pianos	tomato—tomatoes
soprano—sopranos	potato—potatoes
auto—autos	echo—echoes
solo—solos	hero—heroes

Some words, such as *motto*, *mango*, and *mosquito*, may end with either *s* or *es* in their plural form. The safest thing to do is to memorize the few words that always add *es*, and then consult a dictionary when in doubt about others.

Spelling Plurals Correctly. In each sentence below, change the singular noun given in parentheses into the plural form. Write it in the blank after the sentence.

    EXAMPLE: The (potato) are especially good this year. ___*potatoes*___

1. One art of the (Eskimo), called scrimshaw, is famous throughout the world. _____

2. I had my mother's (cameo) set in a ring and a necklace. _____

3. Americans listened to Franklin Roosevelt on their (radio). _____

4. Old (piano) had ivory keys, but new ones have plastic keys. _____

5. Uncle Joe was given a welcome usually reserved for (hero). _____

6. Artists prefer natural light in their (studio). _____

7. Thousands of (auto) heading out of town have created a traffic jam. _____

8. (Mango) grow on evergreen trees that belong to the cashew family. _____

9. Elena Trajillo and Robert Warnike will each sing two (solo) in the concert. _____

10. The (soprano) competed to see who could sing the highest note. _____

11. (Tomato) used to be considered poisonous. _____

12. That cowboy has ridden in (rodeo) all over the West. _____

13. There are eight (alto) in the chorus. _____

14. (Banjo) are used quite often in Dixieland music. _____

15. How much fodder is stored in those (silo)? _____

16. (Folio) are very large books. _____

17. Recording (studio) have soundproof rooms. _____

18. Camping in the canyon, John heard (echo) from far away. _____

Nouns Ending in *f*, *ff*, or *fe*

The plurals of most nouns ending in *f* or *ff* are formed regularly by adding *-s*.

chiefs   staffs   gulfs   sheriffs

The plurals of some nouns ending in *f* or *fe* are formed by changing the *f* or *fe* to *ve* and adding *-s*.

wife—wives   wolf—wolves   leaf—leaves
thief—thieves   life—lives   loaf—loaves
elf—elves   calf—calves   half—halves

Spelling Plurals Correctly. In each of the following sentences, change the singular noun given in parentheses into the plural form. Write it in the blank after the sentence. Consult a dictionary as necessary.

EXAMPLE: The (sheriff) of all the counties in Iowa are holding a convention. _____*sheriffs*_____

1. The (leaf) of deciduous trees fall off in the autumn. _____

2. (Elf) and hobbits are two types of creatures found in J. R. R. Tolkein's stories. _____

3. The (roof) were steeply pitched so they would shed snow easily. _____

4. How many (loaf) of bread does your family eat each week? _____

5. The (life) of pioneer men and women were unbelievably difficult. _____

6. The (staff) of nutrition institutes from all over the nation are meeting in Omaha. _____

7. How many (gulf) can you name in the Eastern Hemisphere? _____

8. The drawer was full of beautiful wool (scarf). _____

9. Have you worked out the (proof) for the geometry problems? _____

10. Many magicians use (handkerchief) in their acts. _____

11. Mattie varnished the (shelf) of the bookcase. _____

12. (Wolf) are actually far less dangerous to humans than is commonly believed. _____

13. Tecumseh was one of many Indian (chief) who tried to keep settlers from taking

more Indian lands. _____

14. Andrea is fascinated by the vast (gulf) of space between stars. _____

15. Swiss Army (knife) are multipurpose instruments. _____

16. Ivan made a centerpiece using dried flowers and (sheaf) of wheat. _____

17. The farmer has eight new (calf) this spring. _____

18. Filling the (half) of a tomato with egg salad makes a good summer meal. _____

Nouns with Irregular Plurals

The plural of some nouns is formed by a change of spelling.

tooth—teeth   crisis—crises
foot—feet   basis—bases
man—men   goose—geese
woman—women   mouse—mice
child—children   phenomenon—phenomena
ox—oxen   datum—data
hypothesis—hypotheses

The plural and singular forms are the same for a few nouns.

sheep   Chinese   Swiss
deer   Portuguese   moose
tuna   corps   Japanese

Spelling Plurals Correctly. Read each of the sentences below. Where necessary, change the singular noun given in parentheses into the plural form. Write the correct plural form in the blank after the sentence. If the plural form is spelled the same as the singular form already used, place a **C** in the blank.

    EXAMPLE: My two (foot) are not quite the same size. _*feet*_____

1. Flossing your (tooth) is just as important as brushing them. _____

2. The (Portuguese) were great explorers in the fifteenth century. _____

3. We saw the (mouse) scampering about in their cages. _____

4. Tell me the (basis) for your decision to become a paramedic. _____

5. How many divisions do those two (corps) comprise? _____

6. (Child) learn through imitation of adults. _____

7. Our village has hired two new (policewoman). _____

8. The fishing boat was loaded with a fresh catch of (tuna). _____

9. A flock of (goose) is known as a goggle. _____

10. (Woman) in Switzerland could not vote until 1972. _____

11. (Ox) are still used to pull carts in some parts of Spain. _____

12. It took four (man) to move that huge marble-topped table into the house. _____

13. Lamar saw three (deer) on Skyline Drive early this morning. _____

14. What do you think are the three most fascinating natural (phenomenon)? _____

15. The (man) in the orchestra wore tuxedos with long tails. _____

Names and Compound Nouns

The plural of a name is formed by adding -s or -es.

William Martin—the Martins   Michael Corey—the Coreys
Bruce Means—the Meanses   Jack Voss—the Vosses

The Plural of Compound Nouns. When a compound noun is written without a hyphen, the plural is formed at the end of the word.

handful—handfuls   doghouse—doghouses   cupful—cupfuls

When a compound is made up of a noun plus a modifier, the plural is added to the noun.

brothers-in-law (*in-law* is a modifier.)
attorneys-general (*general* is a modifier.)

EXCEPTIONS: drive-ins, stand-bys, lean-tos, fill-ins

Spelling Plurals Correctly. In each of the following sentences, change the singular noun given in parentheses into the plural form. Write the correct plural form of the noun in the blank after the sentence. Watch for modifiers.

1. Add two (teaspoonful) of vanilla to the mixture. _____

2. How many (sister-in-law) does Barbara have? _____

3. (Notary public) verify signatures on documents. _____

4. The (Morse) live next door to us. _____

5. Early recipes measured ingredients in (handful) and pinches. _____

6. We have three (doghouse) in our back yard. _____

7. Are all Presidents also (commander-in-chief)? _____

8. The (Hayes), our next-door neighbors, are on vacation. _____

9. Both of Grace's (brother-in-law) are bankers. _____

10. The directions on the bottle say to take two (teaspoonful) at bedtime. _____

11. How many (attorney-general) served between 1960 and 1970? _____

12. (Drive-in) are a particularly American phenomenon. _____

13. (Justice of the peace) are empowered to perform marriages. _____

14. The (Evans) are playing golf with the Millers. _____

15. Which (right-of-way) does the railroad occupy? _____

16. (Lean-to) were available for campers at the state park. _____

17. Mix the water and grated cheese with two (cupful) of flour. _____

18. The (chief of police) of the two cities are meeting today. _____

Spelling Plurals Correctly. In each of the following sentences, change the singular noun given in parentheses into the plural form. Write it in the blank after the sentence.

EXAMPLE: The waiter dropped all the (dish) on his tray. ___*dishes*___

1.   Apses and naves are parts of (church). _____

2.   (Cherry) can be either sweet or tart. _____

3.   Some car (wax) are better than others. _____

4.   The quarterback threw three touchdown (pass). _____

5.   Grover had trouble moving the (box) off the steps. _____

6.   Each of the team's (play) was second-guessed by the opponents. _____

7.   Most of the clubs in our school hold banquets or (party) at the end of the year. _____

8.   Puffed (pastry) with custard filling are called napoleons. _____

9.   The woods are full of (mosquito). _____

10.   These (piano) can be rented with an option to buy. _____

11.   (Tomato) are used in many popular recipes. _____

12.   The (hero) were awarded their medals at the ceremony. _____

13.   Beverly Sills and Leontyne Price are famous (soprano). _____

14.   How many (wife) did Henry VIII have? _____

15.   The Indian (chief) were in full tribal dress. _____

16.   The (knife) were so dull that they were useless. _____

17.   (Shelf) of books lined the musty library. _____

18.   Is it true that a cat always lands on its (foot)? _____

19.   Children get their first (tooth) at about six months. _____

20.   The word kindergarten means "garden of (child)." _____

21.   I love walking through piles of (leaf) in the fall. _____

22.   Barney added two (teaspoonful) of cinnamon to the batter. _____

23.   The (sergeant-at-arms) were dressed in red uniforms. _____

24.   Some grand old (house) had winding staircases. _____

25.   The two (brother-in-law) grew to be great friends. _____

Numbers in Writing

Numbers that can be expressed in fewer than four words are usually spelled out; longer numbers are written in figures.

Tickets for the play cost *three* dollars.
That actress has *thirty-seven* pairs of shoes!
Our house-to-house drive collected *$1,879*.

A number beginning a sentence is spelled out.

Three hundred students attended the assembly.

Figures in Writing. Figures are used to express dates, street and room numbers, telephone numbers, page numbers, decimals, degrees, and percentages.

In April, 1975, our address was 645 Prospect Avenue.
The class in room 318 is at work on algebra problems.
Only 60 percent of the students attended the debate.

Writing Numbers Correctly. Most of the following sentences contain an error in the writing of a number or figure. Underline the error and rewrite it correctly in the blank after the sentence. Three sentences are correct and need no revisions. If a sentence is correct as it is, write **C** in the blank.

1. Thirty-seven people responded to the ad in the newspaper. _____

2. Mr. Bruce's estate amounted to $500,000. _____

3. Connie's room number is two hundred twenty-nine. _____

4. Mexico became a republic in one thousand twenty-three. _____

5. 4 people were injured in the accident. _____

6. Mrs. Miller wrote a check for two thousand, four hundred sixty-seven dollars. _____

7. The election was held on November sixth, nineteen hundred eighty-four. _____

8. The temperature in the room was one hundred one degrees! _____

9. More than three hundred people attended the auction. _____

10. Admission to the fair will be $3.00 for all students. _____

11. Work the problems on page thirty-one for tomorrow. _____

12. I'm sure that at least eighty percent of the teachers believe as we do. _____

13. The women of the art league made $2,236 on their bazaar. _____

14. The selling price of the house was ninety-eight thousand, three hundred dollars. _____

15. 650 tickets for the concert were sold during the first day. _____

16. Of the students at Lincoln High, sixty percent are studying a foreign language. _____

Abbreviations in Writing

Abbreviations may be used for most titles that come before and after proper names, for names of government agencies, and in dates.

BEFORE PROPER NAMES:	Dr., Mr., Mrs., Ms., Rev., Capt., Hon., Gov.
AFTER PROPER NAMES:	Jr., Sr., D. D. S., Ph. D.
DATES AND TIMES:	P. M., B. C.
GOVERNMENT AGENCIES:	FBI, FCC, NASA (there are no periods after government agency abbreviations)

The titles *Honorable* and *Reverend* are not abbreviated when preceded by *the*.

In ordinary writing, abbreviations are not acceptable for names of countries and states, months and days of the week, nor words that are part of addresses or firm names.

UNACCEPTABLE	BETTER
We went to N. Y.	We went to New York.
The date was Tues., Dec. 5.	The date was Tuesday, December 5.
The Pub. Serv. Co. sent a bill.	The Public Service Company sent a bill.

In ordinary writing, do not abbreviate words standing for measurements or names of school courses. Also, do not abbreviate the words *Christmas*, *page*, and *chapter*.

Correcting Errors in Abbreviations. Underline the errors in the abbreviations in the following sentences. Correct each error in the blank after the sentence.

1. Al will start work for Roland Laboratories in Oct. _____

2. Len is the sec. of our French club. _____

3. The Hon. Margaret Sims has had four terms in office. _____

4. Gretchen is registered for Engl. 101 next fall. _____

5. The devastating tornado lasted only five min. _____

6. The Blacks are moving to N. J. _____

7. Has Karen had a raise in the last yr? _____

8. Opening night will be on Fri., Dec. 3. _____

9. The Rev. Theodore Hesburgh spoke to the graduates about their future. _____

10. Bob works for the Hopkins Mfg. Co. _____

11. Where will you spend Xmas vacation this year? _____

12. The Pres. of the United States is one of the most important people in the world. _____

13. Dee has been to the West Coast, but she's never been to Ariz. _____

14. Luis Ortega is the treas. of our class. _____

15. The Vice-Pres. of the United States often represents our nation abroad. _____

The Use of Italics

The word *italics* is a printer's term. It refers to a kind of type. When a writer wants the printer to set a word in italic type, he or she underlines it in the manuscript.

Titles of complete books and plays, of newspapers, magazines, works of art, and long musical compositions are printed in italics. The names of ships, trains, and airplanes are also printed in italics.

His poetry has appeared in *The New Yorker*.
Newsweek helps me keep up with the news.
My Fair Lady is based on Shaw's *Pygmalion*.

Foreign words that are widely used, such as *entrepreneur* and *chauffeur*, are printed in regular type. Words and phrases that have not become naturalized in our language are printed in italics: *cum laude*, *bon vivant*.

Italics are used for words, letters, or figures referred to as such.

There are too many *and's* in your first sentence.

Italics (underlining) are used to give special emphasis to words or phrases. Use italics for emphasis only to make the meaning clear.

I've *always* admired him.
Did you say you owe *me* some money?

Using Italics Correctly. In each of the following sentences, underline the words that should be placed in italics.

EXAMPLE: Jim graduated cum laude from Yale.

1. Maria saw the statue of the Venus de Milo at the Louvre.

2. After reading a review of Freedom at Midnight, I wanted to read the book.

3. My brother graduated magna cum laude from the University of Michigan.

4. Which news magazine do you prefer: Time or Newsweek?

5. The Flying Dutchman is a mythical ship sailed by ghosts.

6. Don't write the word principal when you mean principle.

7. You have three if's in your last sentence.

8. In England the word laboratory is accented on the second syllable.

9. Aaron Copeland wrote a beautiful ballet called Appalachian Spring.

10. Mr. Swenson has read the Des Moines Register for forty years.

11. Did you read the article about earthquakes in Science Digest?

12. What we call a hardware store is called the ironmonger's in Great Britain.

13. The there should have been written their.

14. We all enjoyed seeing the spring musical, Annie Get Your Gun.

15. The Italian word adagio means "slowly and leisurely."

16. The Atlanta Constitution is a well-respected newspaper.

Review: Good Manuscript Form

Writing Numbers Correctly. The following sentences contain errors in the writing of numbers or figures. Underline each error and rewrite it correctly on the blank.

> **EXAMPLE:** Ray was born in <u>nineteen forty-four</u>. *1944*

1. Only three hundred people attended—less than fifty percent. _____

2. Bob earns 3 dollars an hour for mowing lawns. _____

3. Alfred got to page seventy before he fell asleep. _____

4. Because of road repairs it took us 6 hours to drive 100 miles. _____

5. The tax bill was thirty-two thousand, three hundred dollars. _____

6. Life expectancy in some parts of the world is under 40 years. _____

7. The temperature dropped to seventeen degrees below zero. _____

8. Our classroom number is two twenty-two. _____

9. My baby brother was born on October third. _____

10. Barbara paid $45.00 for those jeans, and they shrank. _____

Correcting Errors in Abbreviations. Underline the error in abbreviation in each of the following sentences. Correct the error on the blank after each sentence.

> **EXAMPLE:** Each class in our school is fifty <u>min.</u> long. *minutes*

1. The Rev. Cotton Mather was a famous Puritan writer. _____

2. Claire's next orthodontist appointment is Tues. afternoon. _____

3. The Holland Baking Co. makes delicious whole grain bread. _____

4. Doug hopes to spend the winter in Calif. _____

5. The boatload of immigrants arrived in N.Y. harbor. _____

Using Italics Correctly. In each of the following sentences, underline the words that should be placed in italics.

> **EXAMPLE:** Are <u>you</u> telling <u>me</u> what to do?

1. Last week's issue of The English Journal had an interesting article on SAT scores.

2. Susan graduated summa cum laude from Radcliffe.

3. The adding machine misprinted all of the seven's.

4. The Titanic's sinking was a shock to nautical engineers.

5. Ed is looking forward to reading A Hitchhikers Guide to the Galaxy.

The Topic Outline

There are two types of outlines: topic outlines and sentence outlines. A **topic outline** uses words or phrases instead of complete sentences. It is useful for quick note taking or for informal organizing.

For all types of outlines, follow these guidelines:

1. Center the title of the piece of writing at the top of the outline.
2. Arrange numbers and letters in the following order, from main point to most specific subpoint: I., A., 1., a., (1), (a).
3. Indent all headings in the outline.
4. Do not use a single heading. Divide each heading into at least two parts.
5. Use the same kind of phrase for all headings of the same rank.
6. Begin each entry in the outline with a capital letter.
7. In a topic outline, do not place periods at the ends of entries.

Revising an Outline. The following topic outline contains several errors in form. Rewrite the outline, correcting these errors.

The Life and Work of John Muir   _____

1. early life   _____

   A. In Scotland   _____

   B. In Wisconsin   _____

      1. Love of nature   _____

      2. Interest in science _____

   C. ADULT LIFE   _____

      1 as a naturalist.   _____

      2 As an activist.   _____

         a. He founded the   _____

         Sierra Club.   _____

         b. Lobbied for creation
of national parks   _____

      3. As an author   _____

         I. wrote *Our National Parks* (1901)   _____

         ii. Wrote *The Yosemite* (1912).   _____

A **sentence outline** is one that is made up of complete sentences. It is useful for taking detailed notes and for organizing formal writing. When making a sentence outline, follow the same rules for form that you follow when making a topic outline. However, make sure that all your entries are complete sentences and that each ends with a period.

Completing a Sentence Outline. Put the following sentences where they belong in the outline below.

—At about the age of fifteen, the boy would become a squire.

—At the conclusion of the ceremony, the lord would tap the squire on the shoulders with a sword while saying, "I dub you knight."

—The page would serve his master and learn a code of courtesy and noble behavior known as *chivalry*.

—Many squires were knighted in special peacetime ceremonies.

The Making of a Knight

I. At about the age of seven, the boy would join the household of a great lord as a page.

   A. The lord would teach his page to use weapons, to play games of strategy such as chess, and to hunt with falcons and hawks.

   B. _____

    _____

II. _____

  _____

   A. The squire acted as his master's personal servant.

   B. The squire learned the arts of battle and of horsemanship.

   C. The squire would serve his master for five years.

III. At about the age of twenty the squire could become a knight.

   A. Any knight could bestow knighthood on a squire.

   B. Many squires were knighted on battlefields after proving themselves in battle.

   C. _____

    _____

     1. Before the ceremony, the squire would prepare by bathing, dressing in special clothes, and taking part in religious rituals.

     2. During the ceremony, the squire would kneel and receive a sword and spurs.

     3. _____

      _____